04

FREEMAN, G
BALLET GENIUS : TWENTY GREAT
DANCERS / G. FREEMAN AND E

792.8   7-045574

D0271397

B·A·L·L·E·T G·E·N·I·U·S

By the same authors

Gillian Freeman:
The Undergrowth of Literature
The Story of Albert Einstein
The Schoolgirl Ethic: The Life and Work of Angela Brazil

Edward Thorpe:
The Other Hollywood
The Colourful World of Ballet
(with Clement Crisp)
MacMillan's Isadora
Kenneth MacMillan: A Biography

B·A·L·L·E·T
G·E·N·I·U·S

Twenty Great Dancers
of the Twentieth Century

G·I·L·L·I·A·N F·R·E·E·M·A·N

and

E·D·W·A·R·D T·H·O·R·P·E

EQUATION

First published 1988

© GILLIAN FREEMAN and EDWARD THORPE 1988

*All rights reserved. No part of this publication may be reproduced, stored in
a retrieval system or transmitted, in any form or by any means, electronic,
mechanical, photocopying, recording or otherwise, without prior permission
in writing from the Thorsons Publishing Group Limited*

British Library Cataloguing in Publication Data

Freeman, Gillian
Ballet genius: a personal choice.
1. Ballet dancers. Biographies
I. Title   II. Thorpe, Edward
792.8′2′0922

Essex County Library

ISBN 1-85336-008-2
ACKNOWLEDGEMENTS
The illustrations on the following pages appear by kind permission of:
Dancing Times Limited 26, 43, 98, 101, 104; Royal Academy of Dancing
31, 38, 60, 67, 89 (right); Trustees of the Victoria and Albert Museum 8,
17, 48, 55; Anthony Crickmay 89 (left), 108, 111, 114 (right), 118, 122,
132, 137 (bottom), 140, 147, 172, 177, 186, 191, 196, 200, 204; Zoë
Dominic 114 (left), 127, 137 (top), 181, 211, 223 (top), 228, 233 (left);
Catherine Ashmore 233 (right); Russian Embassy 73, 77; Martha Swope
82, 154, 158, 162, 166, 218, 223 (right).

*Equation is an imprint of the Thorsons Publishing Group Limited,
Wellingborough, Northamptonshire, NN8 2RQ, England*

Printed in Great Britain by Butler & Tanner Limited, Frome, Somerset

1 3 5 7 9 10 8 6 4 2

FD 38261

C·O·N·T·E·N·T·S

For

ANNE and PHILIP TODD

Remembering special performances

The Authors would like to thank Robert Penman for his invaluable help in research. We are also grateful to William Poole, Librarian at the Royal Academy of Dancing, for the research facilities placed at our disposal.

I·N·T·R·O·D·U·C·T·I·O·N

Ballet, like all forms of theatre, is a transient art and great performances must necessarily exist, briefly, in the eye and then be cherished in the memory. Some dancers become legends in their own lifetime, others achieve greatness in restrospect. This collection of some of the supreme exponents of the classical style does not try to be comprehensive—the list could easily be quadrupled—but ranges widely within the confines of the twentieth century.

Some artists have been chosen for their historical importance and the impetus they gave to the art, some for their technical virtuosity, some for their outstanding histrionic ability. All of them have contributed something individual to an art which, during the last 75 years, has developed into one of the most powerful and universally expressive forms of entertainment.

GILLIAN FREEMAN   EDWARD THORPE

V·A·S·L·A·V N·I·J·I·N·S·K·Y

The sensation caused by Serge Diaghilev's Ballets Russes amongst the glittering social and intellectual élite during the first Paris season in 1909 was composed of several elements, the most astonishing of which was the brilliance and beauty of the dancing. Above all it was the male dancers that caused the greatest surprise (for more than 50 years male dancing had been in total decline in the West) and the brightest star in Diaghilev's stellar troupe was undoubtedly Vaslav Nijinsky—a dancer and artist of genius and the first male superstar of the ballet since the death of August Vestris in 1842.

Diaghilev was immediately aware of Nijinsky's box-office potential and deliberately added a degree of off-stage mystery to his on-stage magic: Nijinsky rarely appeared in public and only occasionally at the most brilliant salons and receptions. By nature withdrawn and reserved, he was attended night and day, on Diaghilev's orders, by Diaghilev's valet, Vassili Zuikov, and this of course only added to the aura of excitement that surrounded him. It was a great coup for any Parisian hostess who could claim him as a guest and usually meant that she, or her husband, had made a major contribution to the funds of the Ballets Russes.

Vaslav Nijinsky was born in Russia, at Kiev, on 12 March 1888, although both his parents, Thomas and Eleonora, were of Polish nationality, and both were dancers. There were two other children, Stanislav, the elder, and Bronislava, the youngest, who was later to become a distinguished choreographer—all born within a space of six years. When Stanislav was six years old he fell out of a window, landing on his head, and thereafter was mentally retarded, eventually being committed to a state asylum.

Thomas Nijinsky had his own small company and the family toured the length and breadth of Russia, living the typical nomadic life of travelling artists. Thomas was a handsome man and something of a philanderer and when his mistress joined the company Eleonora left and settled in St Petersburg with the children.

At the age of nine Eleonora took Vaslav to be auditioned as a pupil at the Imperial Ballet School. He was immediately accepted—noticed by the great teacher Nicholas Legat (who later opened a school of dance in London) who was impressed by the boy's 'phenomenal leap'.

During his years at the Imperial School, Nijinsky was something of an outsider. His Polish background—despite having been born in Russia—and his Tartarish features (the high cheekbones and the slanting almond-shaped eyes earned him the nickname of 'the little Japanese') set him apart and during his eight years

Nijinsky in Le Dieu Bleu.

of tuition he never made a friend. On the contrary, his spirited self-defence against bullies frequently resulted in poor marks for bad behaviour. Nevertheless, his growing prowess as a dancer did not go unnoticed by his teachers, particularly Mikhail Oboukhov who was always severely critical of his pupils but who gave Nijinsky the highest class marks he had ever accorded.

Nijinsky's graduation performance took place at the Maryinsky Theatre on 29 April 1907. It was a great success. He appeared in excerpts from several ballets, including Petipa's version of *Paquita*, and an early version of Fokine's *La Pavillon d'Armide* (later developed as one of the ballets forming the first Paris programme). After the performance the *prima ballerina assoluta*, Mathilde Kchessinskaya, who had also been the mistress of the Tsar Nicholas II, congratulated Nijinsky and announced that she wished to have him as her partner. There could be no greater accolade for him and it also assured his fortune as a dancer. The gesture was repeated half a century later when the prima ballerina of the Kirov (Maryinsky) Theatre, Natalia Dudenskaya, asked the newly-graduated Rudolf Nureyev to be her partner.

Immediately after his accession to the Imperial Ballet Nijinsky was sent on holiday. In June he was summoned by Kchessinskaya to partner her at Krasnoe Selo, where members of the company entertained army officers and their families during summer manoeuvres.* Eleonora rented a cottage for the season and when it was over Nijinsky visited his father, who had heard of his son's growing reputation, at Nijni-Novgorod. Father and son made friends and danced for each other; Thomas promised to go and see Vaslav dance in St Petersburg but, in fact, that proved to be their last meeting.

During this period Diaghilev had founded his controversial periodical *Mir Isskoustva* (The World of Art) and was laying the foundations of his later entrepreneural enterprises that would culminate in the formation of the Ballets Russes.

Although during Nijinsky's first season with the Imperial Ballet he was officially only a member of the *corps de ballet*, because of his association with Kchessinskaya he was given a number of soloist roles, dancing in *Paquita, La Fille mal gardée, Giselle, Raymonda, La Bayadère* and *The Little Hump-backed Horse*. On 21 March 1908, he took part in the first performance of the revised version of Michel Fokine's *Chopiniana*, known in the West as *Les Sylphides*, the first 'abstract' ballet and destined to become one of the most popular ballets of all time.

---

* An indication of how ballet was a part of middle-class lifestyle in Russia. One can scarcely imagine the Royal Ballet entertaining Army officers on Salisbury Plain!

Nijinsky began to be noticed by regular members of the ballet audience, many of whom were wealthy aristocrats, amongst whom was Prince Pavel Dmitrievitch Lvov. Using the services of a dancer in the company who was frequently employed as a pimp by rich members of St Petersburg society, Lvov contrived an introduction to Nijinsky and subsequently began a homosexual affair with the young man whom he showered with expensive presents. (At that time affairs between men were accepted as quite natural in St Petersburg society.) Later, Lvov introduced Nijinsky to Count Tishkievitch who also gave the dancer gifts, and then to Diaghilev; almost immediately the two men became lovers. It must be said that whereas Nijinsky's attraction for Lvov and Tishkievitch had been mainly physical, for Diaghilev there was also the fascination of a liaison with a beautiful young man who was also a dazzling artist.

Nijinsky later wrote in his diary that he had engaged in this affair with Diaghilev 'because I knew my mother and I would die of hunger, otherwise.' That was nonsense; with his salary from the Imperial Ballet he was well able to provide for both of them to live in comfort, but he was writing at a time when there had been a bitter and irreparable separation from Diaghilev and when his mind was descending into darkness. But whatever interpretation is put upon their relationship there is no doubt that it was the beginning of an association that would change the history of ballet in the Western world.

In 1908 Diaghilev had achieved great success in taking Russian opera to Paris. The following year he was anxious to display the glories of the Russian ballet as well, and he planned to take a mixed repertoire of opera and ballet to the French capital. As it happened, however, through the malicious intervention of the Grand Duke Andre Vladimir, who persuaded Tsar Nicholas II to withdraw a promised financial guarantee, Diaghilev had to change his plans and the Paris programme was eventually nearly all ballet.

After the sensational first night of *Le Pavillon d'Armide*, the *Polovtsian Dances* from *Prince Igor* and a ballet of *divertissements* called *Le Festin*, the programmes which followed were no less amazing to the Parisian audiences and included Fokine's *Les Sylphides** (still called in Russia by its original title of *Chopiniana*) and his *Cléopâtre*, in which Nijinsky's role was that of a slave to the great Egyptian Queen.

At the end of the season Nijinsky became ill. The doctor diagnosed typhoid fever and as the management of the hotel where he was staying were afraid

* It was in *Les Sylphides* that Anna Pavlova made her first appearance in Paris with the company, arriving a fortnight after the other principals. This late arrival enabled Tamara Karsavina to establish her artistry with the Parisian public.

of infection, Diaghilev rented a small furnished apartment where he nursed his invalid dancer. It was during this period that Diaghilev proposed to Nijinsky that they should live together and he agreed.

Despite the artistic and critical success of the season the costs had exceeded the receipts (throughout the 20 years of the existence of his company Diaghilev was forever in financial straits although the Ballets Russes was acclaimed throughout the world) and Diaghilev was bankrupt. Undaunted, he made elaborate plans for the following year, commissioning music from Debussy, Ravel, Fauré and Stravinsky for new projects. When Nijinsky had recovered from his illness Diaghilev took him to Carlsbad and then to Venice where, in the company of one of his great early designers, Léon Bakst, they visited the Accademia, the Scuolo di San Rocco, and many churches. Throughout the years of their relationship Diaghilev did much to stimulate Nijinsky's knowledge and awareness of the arts, taking him to museums, galleries and exhibitions.

While Diaghilev's elaborate plans for a 1910 season in Paris and London went ahead—including a collaboration between the young Igor Stravinsky and Fokine which resulted in *The Firebird* — throughout the winter Nijinsky resumed his duties as a dancer with the Imperial Ballet in St Petersburg in a repertoire that included the grand classical ballets of Marius Petipa as well as the new works by Fokine. During this period Nijinsky lived with his mother.

After endless discussions, arguments, arrangements, upsets, rearrangements, disappointments and broken promises, Diaghilev's plans for his next ballet season in Paris—this time at the famous Opera—were finally complete. The new works in the first programme were both by Fokine, *Carnaval,* a suite of dances for *commedia dell'arte* characters, to an orchestration of Schumann's piano score, and a dance-drama, *Schéhérazade,* to Rimsky-Korsakov's music, with designs by Bakst, a barbaric and voluptuous setting that was to influence interior décors and women's fashions for a decade or more.

It was in this ballet that Nijinsky, as the Golden Slave, scored one of his most sensational successes, variously described by celebrated members of the audience as 'a savage', 'a devil', 'a stallion', 'a cat', 'a snake', 'a hare', 'a panther'—even 'a fish'! From all of which we can deduce that he had a sinuous, flashing, leaping sensuality, a role that was perfect for his combination of physical powers and animal magnetism. Marcel Proust, who was amongst the first-night audience, said 'I never saw anything so beautiful.' Certainly Nijinsky's exotic presence and phenomenal virtuosity excited the Parisians to new heights of rapture in this barbaric ballet with its mixture of melodrama and sex. To modern eyes, in this permissive age, it looks somewhat ludicrous.

In immense contrast to Fokine's new concept of ballet, Diaghilev had decided to include in the season a revival of the Romantic classic *Giselle*, a ballet which had had its world première in Paris in 1841 but which had not been danced there since 1868. The title role was taken by Karsavina (learning it for the first time; in the Imperial Ballet Pavlova had kept the part to herself) with Nijinsky as Count Albrecht. Although both dancers scored a personal success in their roles and there was critical acclaim for the production with its beautiful décor by Alexandre Benois, Nijinsky was not really suited to formal cavaliers and after the wild excitements of *Cléopâtre*, *Polovtsian Dances* and *Schéhérazade*, *Giselle* seemed somewhat insipid to Parisian audiences—especially the score by Adolphe Adam.

Schéhérazade had been a great success but an even greater one, because of what it portended for the future, was *The Firebird*, with its wonderful, innovative score by Stravinsky—the first time this young man's music had been heard in the West. Diaghilev, of course, was pleased by the ballet's success but there was no part in it for Nijinsky and it had been Karsavina's triumph in the title role. Diaghilev resolved that, the following year, he would have a new ballet to show off the talents of his great male star.

For 1911 Diaghilev decided not only to have a new vehicle for Nijinsky but also to form his own permanent company. Because of their contractual obligations to the Imperial Ballet, Diaghilev could not rely on borrowing them from St Petersburg; he had to recruit his own dancers. Karsavina had been appointed a prima ballerina and so could arrange her comparatively rare performances to fit in with other engagements, while Adolph Bolm, having served his obligatory five years after graduation, was free to leave should he wish to do so. Nijinsky was the problem: there was still two years of his contract to run. Then fate took a hand.

Nijinsky was scheduled to dance in *Giselle* and he elected to wear the costume Benois had designed for him for the Paris performance, which was without the trunks or knickerbockers it was customary to wear over the tights in Russia. A stage official asked him to wear the trunks and Nijinsky refused; his appearance offended the Dowager Empress who was present at the performance and the next day he was peremptorily dismissed from the company. Thus Diaghilev acquired his star dancer on a permanent basis. Whether the incident was entirely fortuitous or whether Nijinsky deliberately provoked the authorities of the Imperial Ballet is uncertain. What is certain, is that he was now free to pursue a much more artistically adventurous course under Diaghilev's direction.

The ballet that evolved as a vehicle for Nijinsky was *Petrouchka*, an ugly, sawdust-filled clown in love with a ballerina who, in turn, is attracted by a splendid blackamoor, all three of them puppets operated by a sinister charlatan giving his show in a booth at the St Petersburg Shrovetide Fair. The scenario was evolved by Benois who was also responsible for the wonderful fairground décor. The music was once again by Stravinsky, even more innovative than *The Firebird*—when the orchestra first began to rehearse the score they burst out laughing, thinking it was some sort of musical joke.

Once more the astonishing music, the brilliant staging and the very Russian narrative thrilled the Parisian audiences, and the four principals—Karsavina as the Ballerina, Nicholas Orloff as the Blackamoor, Enrico Cecchetti as the Charlatan and Nijinsky as Petrouchka—received great acclamation, especially Nijinsky whose performance as the pathetic puppet who is revealed as having a soul, was considered as one of the great stage performances of the time.

It is well to remember that this part was unlike any other male character in ballet—no grand cavalier, no sensual slave even, but an ugly, drooping little figure with odd, jerky movements, his gloved hands flopping about, his feet turned in. In particular it was in total contrast to Nijinsky's portrayal of the title role in *Le Spectre de la Rose* which had been given a few days before (the world première had taken place in Monte Carlo). In that ballet Nijinsky had 'become' the very spirit of the flower, not a man dressed in rose petals but some evanescent being who, in the words of Jean Cocteau, gave 'the impression of some melancholy, imperious scent'.

This third Paris season confirmed Nijinsky's fame as 'the God of the Dance,' an amazing creature possessed of phenomenal physical powers, able to absorb a role so completely that he 'became' the character or being that he was portraying. In today's demotic he had become a megastar, idolized by the audiences, known by name by those who did not go to the ballet.

That same summer Diaghilev's Ballets Russes made its first visit to London, at Covent Garden on 21 June 1911. The company had been scheduled to appear the year before but the season was cancelled owing to the death of King Edward VII. With a repertoire that included *Le Pavillon d'Armide, Carnaval, Prince Igor, Schéhérazade, Les Sylphides* and *Le Spectre de la Rose*, the company achieved much the same sensational success as in Paris—although on the first night several elderly dowagers, encrusted with jewels, left the theatre during *Prince Igor,* upset by the 'barbarism' of the warriors!

Later that year the company made an extensive tour of Europe, including Vienna, where Nijinsky learned of the death of his father, and Dresden, where Diaghilev and Nijinsky made their first visit to Emile Dalcroze's School of

Eurythmics. In Budapest a young woman saw Nijinsky for the first time and was captivated . . . Within 18 months her interest in the dancer was to change his whole life, both private and professional.

Nijinsky was not wholly satisfied with his status as the most brilliant star of Diaghilev's company: more and more he wanted to choreograph. Many of the strange, anti-balletic movements devised for the character of Petrouchka had been his rather than Fokine's, and this made him all the more anxious to create a ballet that was his alone. This suited Diaghilev very well; his relationship with Fokine had, for various reasons, become strained and now here was Nijinsky, waiting in the wings, preparing to supplant Fokine should the occasion arise.

In secret Nijinsky began to choreograph a ballet to Debussy's short orchestral poem after Mallarmé, *L'Après-midi d'un Faune* (Afternoon of a Faun). The theme of a lascivious faun, awakened by a group of nymphs, was treated choreographically in a novel two-dimensional way, as if the figures had stepped from a frieze or a classical urn. There was absolutely no use of familiar classical ballet steps. Nijinsky had indeed created something entirely new—and controversial.

The ballet was controversial on three counts: one was the objection by musical purists that Nijinsky had distorted Debussy's music (the same complaint had been made about Fokine's use of the Rimsky-Korsakov score for *Schéhérazade*); the second was by dance purists that, in abandoning the classical technique Nijinsky had produced something that was not dance at all; and the third was an objection by self-appointed guardians of public morality that the ballet was obscene and indecent. In the closing moments of the work Nijinsky, as the faun, took one of the nymph's veils, or scarves, stretched it out upon his rock, lay down upon it and gave a convulsive, orgasmic jerk.

At the première there were boos, cheers, catcalls and whistles from the audience. Diaghilev, doubtless alert to making profitable publicity from the furore, immediately ordered a repetition of the 12-minute ballet. If *L'Après-midi d'un Faune* was a *succès de scandale* it was not long before most critics and audiences recognized it as a minor masterpiece. It remains the only ballet by Nijinsky of which there is a choreographic record.

The secret preparation of Nijinsky's ballet and its décor by Bakst representing some sylvan grove in ancient Greece enraged Fokine who felt that the impact of his own ancient Greece-based ballet, *Daphnis and Chloe*, to a commissioned score by Ravel, had been lessened. Whereas Nijinsky's ballet was short, Fokine's was long and elaborate, Ravel's score demanding a huge orchestra and chorus and lasting nearly an hour. Its first night, a mere week after that of Nijinsky's, was bedevilled by practical difficulties and backstage intrigues. The break with

Diaghilev was inevitable but the wily impresario was unconcerned: in Nijinsky he had a sensational dancer, a controversial choreographer and a paramour all in one.

During the summer of 1912 Diaghilev and Nijinsky were lionized by London society, including the Bloomsbury group and Lady Ottoline Morrell. It was in this period that Nijinsky had ideas about his next ballet, *Jeux*, a game of 'tennis' between three dancers to a score by Debussy. Actually it was not a recognizable game of tennis, so much as an amorous *pas de trois* with subtle overtones between the relationships of two women and a man.

At the same time Stravinsky was composing his monumental score *Le Sacre du Printemps* (Rite of Spring). Diaghilev was concerned about the immense difficulties the music would present to Nijinsky as choreographer. During the company's German tour that year the two men paid another visit to Dalcroze's studio; Diaghilev thought that Dalcroze's specialized form of body movement (similar to today's aerobics) might be of help to Nijinsky in the anti-classical style that he was developing.

In Dalcroze's studio was a young Polish woman, Miriam Ramberg, who was deputed to assist Nijinsky with his choreography. Later, she was to change her name to Marie Rambert and become the founder of her own London-based company, one of the most formative influences on the development of ballet and, later, modern dance, in Britain.

Within a few days of meeting Rambert, Nijinsky was to be introduced to another young woman, the aristocratic Romola de Pulsky, who had so admired Nijinsky when the Ballets Russes had visited Budapest the year before. Absorbed, not to say obsessed, with the arts, Romola had also taken ballet lessons and longed to be associated with Diaghilev's company. She followed the company to Vienna and contrived an interview with Diaghilev who agreed that she should take private lessons with the company's ballet-master, Cecchetti. Thus she was able to travel with the company and be near her idol, Nijinsky.

Jeux received its première in Paris on 15 May 1913. It was not a success with the public who did not understand Nijinsky's sculptural poses and stylized movements. Nor was the scenario very clear, either, in the peculiar game of tennis the dancers were playing, or the relationships that were hinted at. Debussy did not like the ballet which he described as 'pointless goings-on'.

But if *Jeux* was a disappointment *Le Sacre du Printemps*, which had given Nijinsky, aided by Rambert, immense difficulty in its composition and which was premièred two weeks after *Jeux*, on 29 May, was a literal riot. The combination of Stravinsky's titanic, dissonant, poundingly rhythmic score and the angular

Nijinsky

Left *Nijinsky in* Le Spectre de la Rose.

Right *Nijinsky, Golden Slave in* Schéhérazade.

choreography, even more strangely stylized than *Jeux*, had the theatre in an uproar. Fist fights broke out amongst the male factions in the audience and rich society women screamed insults at each other. Amidst the pandemonium Nijinsky stood in the wings shouting the complicated counts to the bewildered and frightened dancers. The police were called in to restore order, but in vain. The performance continued to an accompaniment of screams, shouts, laughter, catcalls and insults.

The reception given to the ballet was a bitter disappointment to Nijinsky and Diaghilev—although, as with *L'Après-midi d'un Faune*, he was aware of the value of the publicity the ballet had received. There followed a long disputatious correspondence in the press between the professional critics and a number of celebrities.

A London season followed, the reception given to *L'Après-midi d'un Faune* and *Le Sacre du Printemps* respectful if not enthusiastic. During the channel crossing to England and the company's stay in the capital, Romola de Pulsky frequently contrived to be noticed by Nijinsky, sitting near him on the deck of the ship, lunching and dining at the Savoy Hotel where Diaghilev and Nijinsky were staying.

A fortnight after the London season the company was due to make its first trip to South America on the SS *Avon*. Diaghilev, who had a superstitious dread of water, decided not to make the journey (though he spent the latter part of the summer in that city-on-the-water, Venice). Had he known it, his decision was to have a fatal effect on his relationship with Nijinsky and on the dancer's career.

Throughout the long sea voyage Romola contrived to meet Nijinsky, to watch him perform his daily *barre*, and rehearse the new Bach ballet he was working on, to sit near him on the deck and in the dining room (she was one of the few members of the company travelling first class). There seems no doubt that she was 'pursuing' him; whether she merely wanted to be a favoured companion of this famous artist, to be his lover or even contemplated marriage, it is difficult to decide. Those who travelled with them and were in a position to observe the developing relationship—in particular Marie Rambert; Rhene-Baton the conductor, and his wife; Baron Gunsbourg, a rich dilettant and backer of the Ballets Russes; Adolf Bolm, Nijinsky's fellow principal dancer—none of them dreamed of what was to happen before the ship reached Rio de Janiero.

Nijinsky confided in Marie Rambert that he was in love with Romola, but she did not take him seriously. Then, two days before the ship docked in Rio, Baron Gunsbourg approached Romola in the bar and said that 'as Nijinsky cannot speak for himself he has requested me to ask for your hand in marriage.' Romola thought it was an elaborate joke and, rather upset, she retired to her cabin. There she received a note from Gunsbourg requesting her answer. She went on deck and met Nijinsky who said, in his halting French, 'Mademoiselle . . . voulez-vous, vous et moi . . .?' and pointed to the fourth finger of his left hand, a mimed gesture that could have come from a classical ballet.

Of course, the company were astounded at the revelation—and some were dismayed. Rambert burst into tears, realizing that she, too, loved Nijinsky. Bolm did his best to dissuade Romola from going through with the marriage. All of them realized what a tremendous blow the news would be to Diaghilev.

A civil marriage ceremony was performed in the City Hall, Buenos Aires, on Wednesday, 10 September 1913, followed by a reception at the Majestic Hotel, attended by the whole company. In the evening there was a religious wedding in the church of St Miguel, where the Austro-Hungarian bride married her Russian groom, both of them Catholics.

Nijinsky sent a letter to Diaghilev informing him of the marriage, believing, with astonishing naïvety, that 'he would understand'. Diaghilev received the letter in Venice and was thrown into a fit of hysterical rage and black despair.

The company scored a great success throughout its South American tour although, one evening in Rio, for some inexplicable reason, Nijinsky decided not to dance. This was reported to Diaghilev, who was then in St Petersburg.

During the voyage back to Europe Romola discovered that she was pregnant. She and Nijinsky left the ship at Cadiz and travelled by train to Paris where they expected to meet Diaghilev, but he was not there. From Paris they journeyed to Vienna, where they were met by Romola's sister, and then went on to Budapest where they met Romola's mother.

Nijinsky became increasingly anxious about the two new ballets on which he was working, the Bach ballet, and *The Legend of Joseph*, to a score commissioned from Richard Strauss. The preparatory work was finished but he had not been able to rehearse during the South American tour. He sent a telegram to Diaghilev in St Petersburg asking when rehearsals could start. Diaghilev instructed his régisseur, Serge Grigoriev, to send the following reply:

In reply to your telegram to Monsieur Diaghilev I wish to inform you of the following. Monsieur Diaghilev considers that by missing a performance at Rio and refusing to dance in the ballet Carnaval *you broke your contract. He will not therefore require your further services. Serge Grigoriev, Régisseur of the Diaghilev Company.*

Nijinsky's reaction to this terse telegram was dismay and incredulity. In actual fact Nijinsky had had no formal contract with Diaghilev's company since 1909, but obviously Diaghilev was using the missed performance in Rio as an excuse to take revenge on his lover, whose marriage he took to be an act of treachery and deceit.

Almost the whole of the Ballets Russes repertoire had been built around Nijinsky's talents; now that Diaghilev had summarily dismissed his leading dancer and choreographer he had no compunction in recalling Fokine who, after a four-hour telephone conversation, agreed to return to the company as a replacement for Nijinsky. In addition, Diaghilev engaged a young dancer from the Bolshoi company in Moscow, Leonide Massine, to take over the title role in *The Legend of Joseph*. Massine became Diaghilev's constant companion and Diaghilev began the 18-year-old's artistic education, taking him to galleries and museums, just as he had Nijinsky.

Meanwhile, Nijinsky had received many importunate offers from impresarios from all over Europe, including one from the prestigious Paris Opera, all of which he refused because he wanted to create new ballets, daringly innovative, similar to *Le Sacre du Printemps*. One impresario, however, did succeed in obtaining his services: Alfred Butt of the Palace Theatre, in London, engaged Nijinsky and an *ad hoc* company assembled by Nijinsky and his sister, Bronislava, for an eight-week season in the spring of 1914.

The repertoire included a revised version of *Les Sylphides*, with different pieces by Chopin orchestrated by Ravel and with a décor by Boris Anisfeld, and *Le Spectre de la Rose*, danced before a black curtain. The fact that The Palace was a variety theatre and Nijinsky appeared amongst music-hall turns was felt by Romola to be a bitterly humiliating experience.

Nijinsky had rows with the management and during the second week of the engagement he fell ill with influenza; the management invoked a clause in Nijinsky's contract and the season was cancelled. Nijinsky paid the dancers' salaries for the whole season and their return fares to Russia out of his own pocket. That sad season was Nijinsky's last appearance, as a dancer, in London.

Romola went to Vienna for her confinement. Nijinsky was invited to dance for the King of Spain at a private reception. On his way back to Vienna he stopped off in Paris to see Diaghilev's company and attended the first night of *The Legend of Joseph*, which had a poor reception from the critics. Nijinsky also took a class with Cecchetti and Diaghilev sent Massine to watch and learn. There is no record of Nijinsky meeting Diaghilev although, during the interval at the Opera performance, Nijinsky went to Misia Sert's* box where her guests, including Cocteau, gave him a cool reception.

* Misia Sert was a rich, beautiful, staunch friend of Diaghilev's, married first to Alfred Edwards, a newspaper proprietor, later to Jose-Maria Sert, the painter.

On 19 June 1914, in Vienna, Romola gave birth to a baby girl, named Kyra. Nijinsky was initially disappointed that the child was not a boy but was soon reconciled and became a devoted, doting father.

Towards the end of that month, through the good offices of Lady Ripon, Diaghilev engaged Nijinsky for the London season of his company. Before the season began, however, the other dancers gave Nijinsky a very cold reception; Nijinsky could not bear this and left again for Vienna. During his trip to London the assassination of Archduke Ferdinand of Austria-Hungary had occurred in Sarajevo, the event which precipitated the First World War. Back in Vienna Nijinsky was bombarded by Lady Ripon with letters and telegrams begging him to bring his family to London. Instead, Nijinsky planned to return to Russia via Budapest.

War broke out on 4 August and the Nijinskys found the border between Hungary and Russia closed. They were put under house arrest in Romola's sister's home which resulted, after several months, in considerable domestic friction, but Nijinsky found refuge in working on an idea for a ballet based on Richard Strauss's tone poem *Till Eulenspiegel*. Meanwhile, Diaghilev managed to reassemble several members of his company in Switzerland where he encouraged Massine in his first attempts at choreography.

A plan for the Nijinskys to be exchanged, through the Red Cross, for Russian prisoners of war fell through. Nijinsky seemed happy, however, working on various ideas for new ballets. During this time Diaghilev's company made its first appearance in New York, followed by a tour of the United States.

Many highly-placed people, including the King of Spain and the Pope, begged the Austrian authorities to release the Nijinskys. Eventually they did so and Nijinsky, Romola and Kyra made their way to neutral Switzerland *en route* to join Diaghilev's company in time for its second New York season. When their ship docked in New York Diaghilev greeted Romola with flowers and kissed Nijinsky on both cheeks; Nijinsky placed Kyra in Diaghilev's arms.

During that season Nijinsky once again danced several of his most famous roles in *Le Spectre de la Rose*, *Carnaval*, *Les Sylphides* and *Schéhérazade* and the audiences and critics were as captivated and rapturous as they had been throughout Europe. All the great American families, including the Vanderbilts, entertained Nijinsky and his family at glittering social occasions. Their relationship with Diaghilev was formal, however, and there were several arguments over professional matters, including Massine's performance in *L'Après-midi d'un Faune.*

Diaghilev, who showed no interest in Nijinsky's *Till Eulenspiegel* ballet, was anxious to arrange a second American tour as so much of Europe was closed to him. The impresario Otto Kahn proposed a coast-to-coast tour and, in order to avoid friction between Diaghilev and Nijinsky, suggested that Nijinsky should lead the company which, during the interim, returned to Europe for an engagement in Spain. Nijinsky and his family remained in New York where he engaged an American painter, Robert Edmund Jones, to design *Till Eulenspiegel.*

While Diaghilev remained in Europe with a nucleus of dancers, the main company returned to New York three weeks before the opening of the season in October. Confusion reigned during rehearsals for *Till Eulenspiegel.* The dancers were slow in learning the choreography; Nijinsky did not like the designs; then, in rehearsal, he sprained his ankle and was ordered to rest for several weeks. (Part of the New York contract stipulated that he should dance five times per week.) *Till Eulenspiegel* was postponed. When it was finally performed, with Nijinsky in the title role, it was well received by both audience and critics, one of them calling it 'the most brilliant performance given by the Ballets Russes in America'. Romola considered it to be Nijinsky's best work but it was never seen in Europe and never seen by Diaghilev.

After the long, exhausting coast-to-coast tour of America (Nijinsky met Charlie Chaplin in Hollywood) Nijinsky was invited to rejoin the Diaghilev company in Europe for a subsequent season in Spain. As a non-combatant in the war Nijinsky was only allowed to dance in neutral countries. During their stay there Czar Nicholas II abdicated and the Russian revolution took place. When Diaghilev arrived in Madrid his reunion with Nijinsky was an affectionate one. During the season Nijinsky once again danced several of his most famous roles in *Schéhérazade, Carnaval, Spectre de la Rose* and *L'Après-midi d'un Faune.* The King and Queen attended the ballet almost every night, as well as rehearsals.

After the Spanish season Nijinsky and Romola sailed with the Ballets Russes— once again without Diaghilev—for another season in South America. Kyra was left in a Swiss sanatorium that specialized in the care of children. Before leaving there had been several emotional upsets between Diaghilev and Nijinsky about whether or not the dancer was to undertake the tour. Nijinsky did not want to go; Diaghilev insisted that he was under contract and finally settled the issue in a typically ruthless way by having the Nijinskys arrested. Their final parting, therefore, was hardly amicable.

During the tour, the relationship between the Nijinskys and the rest of the company was cool, particularly with Diaghilev's régisseur, Grigoriev. Nijinsky's last performances with the company were in Buenos Aires, where he performed in *Le Spectre de la Rose* and *Petrouchka.*

After returning from South America the Ballet Russes reformed once more in Spain, while Nijinsky and Romola were reunited with Kyra in Switzerland, taking a villa near St Moritz. In Russia the 'second revolution' had taken place and Lenin was in power. For a year the Nijinskys lived happily in their mountain village. Nijinsky practised every day and spent much of the time devising new ballets, one of which was to be based on his own life.

During the winter of 1917/18 Nijinsky received word that his brother, Stanislav, had died of pneumonia; he accepted the news philosophically. Several impresarios approached Nijinsky with offers to dance or to form his own company, but Nijinsky did not want to dance until the war was over and he was free to plan his professional life in the way he envisaged.

The war ended in the autumn of 1918. Nijinsky spent the following winter devising yet another ballet that was never to be realized, a work set in a brothel with the central character an aged and raddled madame 'selling all kinds of love'. Romola had doubts about whether the subject was possible in balletic terms or even whether it would be allowed, but Nijinsky intended *Les Papillons de nuit*, as he called it, for his new ballet company which he decided would be based in Paris—the Russian revolution having precluded any thought of returning to his homeland.

Despite an apparently serene domestic life Nijinsky's mind was in a turmoil, full of unanswerable questions: what was the meaning of love? What was the purpose of life? Why had he been born? Why did God allow war? They are questions that bother most people at some time or another but they rarely become obsessional; in Nijinsky's case they dominated his waking thoughts more and more. His behaviour became progressively eccentric—sudden, uncharacteristic outbursts of violence (he once deliberately drove a sleigh at a madly furious pace so that Romola and Kyra were thrown out into the snow) followed by periods of introspective gloom; a frenzied period of drawing weird faces with red and black eyes; writing a secret diary which he would not show Romola.

One day the servants reported that Nijinsky was behaving oddly in the village; Romola found him wearing a big golden cross and accosting the villagers, asking them if they had been to church. She reported his behaviour to a local doctor who sent a male nurse, pretending to be masseur, to keep watch over Nijinsky. Romola's sister, Tessa, came to stay and there was much social activity, during which he told Tessa he had been 'acting a part' during which 'Romola, the servants and the whole village' believed he was a lunatic.

Despite this statement, Nijinsky's behaviour became increasingly unpredictable, his moods were more volatile, and in conversation he revealed a state of mind verging on religious mania. With growing anxiety, Romola arranged a visit to a psychiatrist, Professor Bleuler, under the pretence that they would both be undergoing examination prior to having another child. Bleuler pronounced Nijinsky as 'incurably insane, suffering from schizophrenia'.

Professor Bleuler's diagnosis effectively brought to a close the career of the world's most brilliant dancer, a man who had not only restored the status of the male dancer in the West but who also promised to be one of the most innovative choreographers of the time. It was a career that had lasted little more than nine years, but his name still persists as a legend, despite the fact that the image of his dancing lies in a handful of faded photographs and the memories of a rapidly diminishing number of people.

For thirty years, from 1919 until his death in London in 1950, Romola looked after Nijinsky as his wife, nurse, companion, protector and provider, through periods of hope, despair, struggle and poverty. On 14 June 1920, Romola gave birth to another daughter, Tamara. In 1923, in Paris, Diaghilev paid Nijinsky one last visit, saying, 'I need you, you must dance again for the Russian Ballet, for me.' Nijinsky replied: 'I cannot, because I am mad.' Nothing, and no one, could raise him from a state of lethargy.

In 1932 Romola heard that Nijinsky's mother had died in Paris. She did not tell Nijinsky, but would sometimes say that Eleonora was well but too old to come and see him.

The Second World War imposed more privations, more dangers, particularly when Nijinsky, Romola and the children were staying with Romola's parents in Nazi-occupied Budapest, by which time Hitler's Germany was at war with Russia. Not only was Nijinsky an enemy alien but the Nazi policy was to exterminate the mentally defective.

Despite the many dangers, and mainly through Romola's courage, guile, opportunism and subterfuge, they managed to survive both the Nazi occupation and, later, in Vienna, the Russian advance. Eventually, when the war had ended, and because Romola's father had been born in London, she managed to obtain a British passport and so Nijinsky's last years were spent in Britain, 35 years after his last performance in the capital.

Nijinsky died in a London clinic from kidney failure. Romola was at his side. He was buried in the St Marylebone cemetery, in the Finchley Road, on Friday, 14 April 1950. The pallbearers were Serge Lifar (Diaghilev's last protégé), Frederick Ashton, Anton Dolin (Diaghilev's great British male dancer), Cyril Beaumont, Michael Somes, and Richard Buckle, who subsequently wrote the definitive biographies of both Nijinsky and Diaghilev. Other great dancers from the Diaghilev days were also present, including Marie Rambert, Tamara Karsavina and Lydia Sokolova (the British-born dancer Hilda Munnings).

In June, 1953, Lifar arranged for Nijinsky's body to be moved to Paris so that he should be laid to rest in the Montmartre cemetery next to the great French dancer Auguste Vestris who was buried there in 1842.

A·N·N·A P·A·V·L·O·V·A

'She injected me with her poison,' said Frederick Ashton. He was 12 years old when the then renowned Anna Pavlova danced at the Teatro Municipal in Lima, Peru during one of the extensive tours on which she took her company to remote parts of the globe. Through her, audiences in India, Malaya, Japan, Egypt, Australia and South America were introduced to classical ballet. Her driving passion was to excite, enlighten and entertain people who had never before seen and would probably never have the chance to see again the art she adored.

'Seeing her on stage was the end of me!' recalled Ashton. 'From the end of that evening I wanted to dance.'

In no other art, in painting, literature, music or drama is the continuation through generations so direct. There is an actual physical link, a tactile human contact which makes it as accurate as a genealogical line. Until the recent invention of choreology, dancers had nothing comparable to a score or a text. An actor who has played Hamlet in his youth does not take a young player through the moves, because Shakespeare's words are there for reinterpretation. But a ballerina who has danced Giselle will teach the role, just as it was once taught to her, or it could be lost forever. There is, too, a physical and spiritual transference that crosses the footlights, and a dancer's first inspiration will often come at a particular performance. Just as the little boy in Lima knew without doubt what his future held as he watched Pavlova's *Fairy Doll*, so Anna Pavlova herself, at the age of eight was determined to be a dancer when she was taken by her mother to see *The Sleeping Beauty* in St Petersburg as a Christmas treat. In the new year they applied to the Imperial Ballet School. Anna was told to come back when she was 10.

The facts of Anna's birth and childhood are very obscure. She was born on 1 January 1881 if we go by the old style calendar, or 12 February 1881 if we use the new. The place was the St Petersburg Military Hospital, and there is an entry in the registry of births for that day. Anna's mother was married to a reserve soldier, Matvey Pavlov, but records show that he was not Anna's father. There is hearsay evidence that a member of a wealthy Jewish banking family, Poliakoff, claimed he was Anna's half-brother. If it is true, it would support the case that Anna's mother worked for the family and became pregnant by the husband. It would certainly account for Anna's prolonged visits to her grandmother's country cottage in Ligovo, while her mother supported herself

A rare photograph of Anna Pavlova in the first-act costume of Giselle, *date unknown.*

in St Petersburg. In her autobiography, Pavlova stated that her summers were spent in the countryside with both her mother and her grandmother, but her 'companion' the aristocrat Victor Dandré in his biography specified the place as Ligovo, and described Anna as a sickly child who grew up in the country for the sake of her health. Anna herself never mentioned ill health.

There is also some confusion over the middle name, the patronymic. Was she Anna *Matveyevna* Pavlova or Anna *Pavlovna* Pavlova? The fact is that she used Pavlovna, and persuaded others to do the same, although other records use Matveyevna, which would be the normal patronymic of the daughter of the soldier to whom her mother, Lyubov Feodorovna, was officially married. On 10 October 1899, a pass was issued stating that she was from the village of Bor in the province of Tversk, the wife of the reserve soldier, Matvey Pavlov, and that she was 'discharged into the cities and towns of the Russian Empire'. According to this document, Anna was the daughter of a 'first marriage'. No brothers and sisters are mentioned. At this time, the wives of peasants did not have the right to leave their husbands without permission. Lyubov Feodorovna's faith was given as Orthodox, and her occupation as washerwoman. One likes to speculate on the quirk of fate that the pretty young washerwoman hired to wash the shirts of rich banker, Poliakoff, resulted in the birth of a child who was to change the course of ballet throughout the world.

Anna had her own version. In 1910 she was telling reporters that she was the daughter of a 'minor official' who died when she was two, which was why she and her mother lived in straightened circumstances during her childhood. There is no documental evidence of the existence of this 'father and husband' and Pavlova's biographer, Keith Money, suggests that what may have 'died' at the age of two was any financial assistance rendered to her mother by the real father. He also speculates on how it was that such poor people as Anna and her mother could afford that cataclysmic visit to the Maryinsky Theatre when the eight-year-old child knew she had to dance.

'It never entered my mind,' she wrote, years later, 'that there were easier goals to attain than that of principal dancer of the Imperial Ballet.'

According to her own account, on her tenth birthday she again pressed her mother into applying to the School. This time Anna Pavlovna Pavlova was accepted, and began her training at the world famous establishment in Theatre Street. The year was 1891.

Then, as now, competition to achieve a place in a major ballet school was formidable. The applicants outnumbered the vacancies by more than ten to one, and the auditions took place before a jury of highly critical dancers and directors, both past and present. If her fragile appearance gave them momentary pause, Anna's abilities outweighed any misgivings and she embarked on the seven-year course which encompassed not only dancing but a thorough academic and artistic education.

It is interesting to record that she did extremely well in her general schooling, and of historic importance to list her teachers. Alexander Oblakov had been one of the four suitors in the original production of *The Sleeping Beauty*. Ekaterina Vazem was a former ballerina of the Company who had studied under Marius Petipa and his assistant Lev Ivanov, the last great choreographers of the nineteenth century (she had in fact been Petipa's favourite pupil). Perhaps the most important was Pavel Gerdt, pupil of the famous Swedish dancer and teacher, Christian Johannsen, who had been instrumental in forming the Russian school and inaugurated the style of tailoring the lesson to the individual pupil. Gerdt, following in this tradition, taught Anna in such a way that her fragility became an asset. Her first important role as a student was in *The Two Stars*, which Petipa revived for the school performance on 29 March 1898. The following year, on 11 April, she gave her graduation performance in Alexander Gorsky's *Clorinda* and Pavel Gerdt's *Imaginary Dryads*. Gerdt had taught the graduation class. Thus she finished her training at the age of 17 and was awarded the high grade of 'First Dancer'.

Valerian Svetlov, a distinguished critic, recalled the debut of Anna Pavlova in the Mikhailovsky Theatre:

'I found myself a cosy little corner, in the lighted warm green realm of the dryads. This little corner was the Mikhailovsky Theatre and the dryads proved to be unreal, for they were represented by ordinary pupils of the theatrical school . . . The jury sat in the front row putting down marks on the dryads. This alone somewhat destroyed the illusion.' It could not have been too distracting, for he continued, 'It was on this evening that for the first time the public saw the pupil, Pavlova, and it was on this evening that for the first time she attracted the attention of everybody . . . one already felt something more, something that made it possible for one, without posing as a prophet, to foresee in the youthful dancer a future great artist.'

The school graduates did not join the company for three months, but on 1 June Anna became an official member, not as a dancer in the *corps de ballet* as was customary, but as a *coryphée*, and made her début on 10 September 1899 in the *pas de trois* from *La Fille mal gardée*, and in the winter of that year she took part in a special season at The Hermitage Theatre, linked by a bridge to the Tsar's Winter Palace. There, on the tiny stage, she danced the Hoarfrost variation in *Les Saisons*, choreographed by Petipa for the occasion. It was later repeated at a special benefit performance, at the end of which the prima ballerina assoluta Mathilde Kchessinska, brought Anna forward to the footlights to receive the applause of the audience, as the dancer who had received most applause during the performance!

The opening of the new season in the autumn of 1900 saw Anna cast as Aurora—not the famous Aurora in *The Sleeping Beauty*, that was to come later—but the second lead in *The Awakening of Flora*, a one-act ballet by Petipa and Ivanov. After a few performances she was promoted to the lead, but the role of Flora had been created for Kchessinska, whose technique and qualities were very different. Not surprisingly, Anna was apprehensive and nervous, although she was dancing with Pavel Gerdt who had inspired her with so much confidence during the years of training. Her fears were well-founded, one critic described her performance as 'positively poor' although another was far-sighted enough to suggest that she should be given roles in future that were more suited to 'the quality of her talent'.

It seems the management took note. In the spring of 1901, she appeared as Gulnare in *Le Corsaire*, the second most important role in the ballet. In the autumn she was promoted to soloist, and during that season she was partnered by the legendary Nicholas Legat and Michel Fokine. Like many artists she enjoyed taking part in experimental work staged by contemporary colleagues outside the mainstream performances, and one such evening included a play by Chekov and ended with a *pas de deux* choreographed by Fokine. Within the company she was cast by Petipa as Princess Florine in Act III of *The Sleeping Beauty*, a memorable evening which had begun with *Sylvia*, re-choreographed by Gerdt and Ivanov.

Her teachers at this time were Christian Johannsen, the perfectionist whose greatest form of praise was to say, 'Now you may do that in public', and Yevgenia Sokolova, famous ballerina of the 1870s and great exponent of Petipa roles. With Kchessinska she prepared Pavlova for the part of Nikiya in one of Petipa's greatest works, *La Bayadère*, in which an oriental temple dancer falls in love with Solor, a warrior, who betrays her. Petipa had scheduled Anna to dance early in the season, but there were set-backs and it wasn't until 28 April 1902 that she made her début in the role, with Gerdt as Solar. Her interpretation gave nuances beyond Petipa's expectations. Dance and mime fused into brilliant characterization. Her unique talent was recognized by the great critic, André Levinson, who wrote 'The unrealizable in drama has become possible in the forms of classical dance. This is the profound symbolism of ballet, realized by Pavlova.'

Left *Anna Pavlova in* Swan Lake.

Right *Anna Pavlova in* La Fille mal gardée.

This rare quality of infusing classical ballet with the emotional gifts of an actress restored the popularity of *Giselle* with St Petersburg audiences. When Pavlova danced the role for the first time on 30 April 1903 her appearance of physical vulnerability, her big, dark expressive eyes and the inner anguish she brought to the betrayed heroine gave the story a freshness to a public over-familiar with the work. One critic referred to the harmony of her talent. Another that 'her powerful dramatic talent in the scene of madness and death makes you live through a moment of tragedy, and her ethereal, transparent, quivering dances in the forest among the Wilis will allow you to experience the rare instance of true artistic emotion of the highest order'.

That night was remarkable in ballet history. Not only did Pavlova seal her reputation with an interpretation which evoked memories of Taglioni, but Tamara Karsavina made her début in the peasant *pas de deux*, partnered by Fokine. Recalling it many years later, she wrote that Anna expressed 'a pathos which could not have been surpassed . . . that pathos and the quality of incorporeal grace were essential features of Pavlova's genius'.

She could not have been totally satisfied herself with the performances, because that summer she travelled to Milan to take class with Caterina Beretta, ballet mistress at La Scala. She was concerned about her technique which had from time to time been criticized, although her dramatic ability was constantly extolled.

One of this century's most extraordinary meetings between artists took place in January 1905, when the extrovert American, Isadora Duncan, and the introverted Russian, Anna Pavlova, were introduced in St Petersburg. Duncan had been invited to perform, and was lavishly entertained by Kchessinska as prima ballerina of the Imperial Ballet. There she met all the great artists who, through the genius of Diaghilev, were soon to transform the ballet in the West—Bakst, Benois, Nijinsky, Fokine, Karsavina, Petipa, as well as Pavlova herself. Pavlova was impressed with Duncan's intensity and conviction and her passionate belief in dance as a serious and expressive art. The performances attracted considerable interest and discussion and reputedly influenced Fokine in his choreographic reaction against the rigid classical style.

Isadora made several visits to the ballet and the Imperial Ballet Schools, and watched, amazed, as Pavlova took her daily class. 'Deformed and artificial!' was her pronounced reaction to the *haute école*, and was convinced that she had contributed to the art of dance in Russia by her use of music by Schumann and Chopin, her free-movement style, and her loose, flowing costumes and bare feet. Some years later, when Anna danced Fokine's *Bacchanale* in St Petersburg wearing Greek sandals instead of ballet shoes, audiences compared her to Isadora, but in reality there was no similarity. Duncan's bacchic frenzy stemmed from inner feelings and improvization, while Fokine's choreography demanded the iron control of a trained ballerina. There was, however, a moment of genuine frenzy, when stunned audiences heard the report of Anna's hand against the cheek of her partner, Mikhail Mordkin, as she culminated an argument in the wings. The cause is not on record, but for seven days they refused to dance together. They must have managed to patch up the quarrel because when they next appeared a critic declared they had never been more brilliantly and excitingly in accord. 'The splendid tumult of it all, the mad delight in power, the divine intoxication with the wonder of the world — was that ever so vivid, ever with such a thrill?'

There was discord on a wider scale which was to have more shattering reverberations. When Isadora had arrived in St Petersburg her carriage was blocked by an immensely long funeral procession. Unable to understand the explanation of a coachman, she did not learn until afterwards that it was the mass funeral of men, women and children massacred by the Tsar's troops when thousands of workers had attempted to petition their ruler outside the Winter Palace—the so-called 1905 Uprising. The resulting political upheaval caused turmoil in St Petersburg and dancers were not unaffected. Pavlova played a leading part in battling with the authorities about the management of the company, was involved in petitioning, and at one point refused to take part in a performance. Her position with the company was sufficiently secure and there was no retaliation. In fact at the end of the 1905/6 season she was promoted to ballerina after a performance of *La Bayadère*.

She had become a private pupil of Enrico Cecchetti, one of the greatest teachers in the history of ballet. At one time or another he taught all of the dancers who were to become part of Diaghilev's company, and he imparted some of the Italian precision and strength to Anna, who was always seeking to improve her technique. He remained her teacher for many years. Even when a dancer rules her own company, as Pavlova was to do, she remains a student, never ceasing to learn, never too self-important to accept correction.

Over the years she had acquired a circle of influential and wealthy friends. One who had followed her career since her first appearance with the company was the aristocrat, Baron Victor Emilovitch Dandré, a fervent balletomane 11 years her senior who was to become her manager and her lover (it is assumed) but never her husband. In 1906 he was instrumental in helping her move to an apartment in a part of St Petersburg more fitting for her status. Associates speculated that they might now marry, but whatever the reason they remained in today's vernacular 'just good friends!'

Pavlova's name is indissolubly linked with *The Dying Swan*. One could go further and say her name is synonymous with it. People who have never seen a ballet in their lives, would not recognize a photograph of Pavlova, know nothing else about her will, when asked, associate her with the swan, which is not dying in the original title. *Le Cygne* was first performed in the Maryinsky Theatre on 22 December 1907. It was arranged by Fokine to music by Saint-Saens (from *Le Carnaval des Animaux*) unlike any conventional ballet music which in itself created an ambiance of excitement. As the slight figure in a white tutu seemed to float across the stage, wings fluttering, back to the audience, they responded to the romantic image of a beautiful bird accepting the inevitability of its death. The occasion was a charitable one, in aid of newborn children and impoverished mothers, sponsored by Her Imperial Highness Olga Alexandrovna, and Pavlova's heart-touching evocation of life's ephemeral essence brought an unexpected added poignancy.

Such was the impact of both work and artist that those who saw her that night never relinquished the memory. André Levinson was there to witness this landmark in the history of ballet, and this is how he recorded it.

Pavlova as the Swan rises on tiptoe, crossing her lowered arms on her feathered tunic, and dreamily describes slow circles. Impelled by the rhythmic swaying of her arms, she rushes into the depths of the stage to meet the imaginary horizon on the backcloth. Prepared for flight, she comes to a halt, as though on the edge of an airy precipice, in a tense, beautiful *attitude*. Suddenly her figure is inclined in pain, and her arms clasped to her body bend excruciatingly in abrupt movements of agony and struggle. Her steps become quick and irregular in her alarm. On legs quivering like strings, she moves backward towards the footlights. Darting on one leg forward in a magnificently curved ascent, she lands on one knee, and with her dying motion, protracted and indescribably moving, she finally comes to rest.

Until now Pavlova had been seen only by Russian audiences, but in 1908 she made her first journey abroad to Riga with a small company of dancers. The following year she visited Scandinavia and Germany, and joined Serge Diaghilev's *ad hoc* company in Paris two weeks after the season had begun. Had she arrived earlier Karsavina would not have had the opportunity of establishing herself with the audiences, and although Pavlova's portrait was on the posters, she found herself overshadowed not only by Karsavina but by Ida Rubinstein in *Cléopâtre* and Vaslav Nijinsky, who was being heavily promoted by Diaghilev. Thus began the much vaunted split with Diaghilev which was never to lose its bitterness. She danced for him only once again as a guest artist in 1911.

In 1910 she decided to resign from the Maryinsky (although she continued her contact with the company until 1913), and enjoyed triumphant seasons in New York and London. In New York there was a bizarre opening performance to an almost empty theatre, because the management of the Metropolitan Opera House had decided that an opera must precede the ballet, and it was almost 11 p.m. when the curtain rose on *Coppelia*, and two-thirds of the spectators had gone home. However, those who remained were ecstatic, and the critics were enthusiastic at a time when ballet was even more the Cinderella of the arts than it is today. *The New York Times* reported in some amazement that in St Petersburg a whole two nights a week were given over to dance.

From New York Pavlova, and her partner, Mordkin, travelled to London to perform at the Palace Theatre where they were rapturously received. She could not have known that the country which welcomed her was to become her home, and the fans and friends she gathered, her compatriots.

When Anna returned to St Petersburg it was to the scandal that her close friend, Victor Dandré, had been arrested on a charge of fraud. A member of the St Petersburg City Council, he had been salting away government funds for his own use. When Anna arrived he was released on bail, on the undertaking that he would not leave the city. The details are not known but, somehow, within a few weeks, both Pavlova and Dandré were in London, he exiled for life, Anna self-exiled through love and loyalty.

They became tenants of Ivy House, in Golders Green, North London, on the edge of Hampstead Heath. In 1914 they bought it and it was here that Anna formed a small ballet company of mainly English girls with which she toured the world. Early in her travels she discovered that the Russian and Polish artists were volatile and argumentative and came to blows, whereas the English were docile and easy to manage. The girls she selected were 'daughters of gentlemen' and she gave respectability to a profession which had hitherto been looked upon with condemnation. Her own partners, however, came mainly from Russia, and she engaged Mordkin, Legat and Adolph Bolm among other celebrated executants.

During the First World War she toured North America with her company, preceding Diaghilev's Ballets Russes, and in 1915 she played the role of Fenella in a film, *The Dumb Girl of Portici*, which helped to finance her company. The administration and the extensive tour schedule was carried out by Dandré who remained an indispensible background figure in all her undertakings. As soon as the war ended Pavlova was back in Ivy House. There exists a short film, made in Hollywood by Douglas Fairbanks in 1924, which, despite the poor lighting and flickering images, gives some idea of the magical quality of her dancing.

Pavlova herself choreographed just one ballet, *Autumn Leaves*, to music by Chopin, a rather kitsch little work of which the title tells all. Much of her repertoire, the costumes, the choice of music was in doubtful taste, as opposed to that of Diaghilev who engaged the finest artists, designers, composers and choreographers of the time to create for his great innovative company. Pavlova's great achievement was to tour her company to the furthest corners of the world to instil in people a love and awareness of the art of ballet that lingered long after her own emphemeral performances. 'She was always exercising, always rehearsing,' wrote Cyril Beaumont, the English critic, 'she must live up to, and not on, the golden legend of her name.' One of Pavlova's legacies to British ballet was her troupe of excellently trained young girls, of inestimable value to the embryo British companies that were born soon after her death.

Pavlova went to Spain, Portugal and France; to India, Malaya, Japan and other countries in the Far East. She danced in South America, Australia and New Zealand. It was in Paris, on her way to the Hague in January, 1931, that she contracted pneumonia, but she refused to call a doctor and insisted on continuing her journey to Holland. There, in the Hotel des Indes in the Hague, her condition worsened and she died on Friday 23 January 1931.

Her last performance took place at The Hippodrome, Golders Green, on 13 December. During the one-week season Frederick Ashton was in the audience, and after the matinée he went backstage to see the woman who had inspired him. He was still in the infancy of his career; she took his hand and promised him that a great future lay before him. She had seen his choreographic debut and intended to engage him for her company.

'I never lose the vision of her', Ashton has said. He spoke for everyone who saw her dance.

'Well my lad, you may make an actor, but by God you'll never be a dancer!'

These words were shouted in anger at 11-year-old Patrick Kay, rehearsing a minuet as Peter the Black Cat in *Bluebell in Fairyland*, his first job in the theatre. The year was 1915. Fred Farren who was arranging the dances probably continued to arrange them in other pantomimes and Christmas plays. The little boy grew up to be Anton Dolin, one of the great British dancers of the twentieth century, a role model at a time when ballet was not considered to be a proper career for a man.

He was the second of three sons born to Helen Maude and George Henry Kay. His mother's maiden name was Healey. She came from Dublin and he adored her. His father was from Hampshire, a cricketer and horseman and master of hounds. During the First World War he lied about his age and served for almost a year with the Royal Fusiliers before it was discovered that he wasn't 42 but 64. Typical of his time and class he forbade the son he called Paddy ever to utter the vile name of Oscar Wilde, and although he managed to accept the possibility that the boy might have a stage career, he was never reconciled to the idea of a dancer. In fact he died two years before Sydney Francis Chippendall Patrick Healey Kay was billed as Anton Dolin at the Royal Albert Hall. He had chosen Anton because he wanted to sound Russian and was reading Anton Chekov at the time. Dolin was the suggestion of the impresario who was putting on the event announced as The Anglo-Russian Ballet. It was really a recital by Princess Serafine Astafieva and her pupils and the box-office did badly. It did, however, obtain a wildly enthusiastic notice in the *Sketch* which suggested that the new dancer, Anton Dolin, might surpass Nijinsky since 'his great work is entirely free from pose'.

He had joined Astafieva's class soon after *Bluebell in Fairyland* ended its run at the Princes (now Shaftesbury) Theatre. Prior to obtaining this first job he had taken ballet lessons with Lillie and Grace Cone, first in Brighton where they taught every Friday evening and then, when the Kay family moved to London, at their main school. Italia Conti had seen him in the show and approached his mother with the suggestion that he should attend the Conti School of Elocution, Acting and Dancing which incorporated a theatrical agency. It was agreed that he should continue his ballet lessons with Miss Cone, but when Mrs Kay took him to the Coliseum to see the Swinburne Ballet with Astafieva as its star, he persisted until he was allowed to attend her studio in the King's Road, Chelsea. Miss Cone reluctantly agreed.

The Conti agency kept him working; three consecutive Christmas seasons

as John in *Peter Pan* at the New (now Albery) Theatre; small parts in silent films and on the stage. During the last year of the war he toured for several weeks in a musical comedy called *Betty*, during which he learned that his much loved elder brother Philip had died in Cairo, and recorded a psychic experience of seeing and hearing him soon after receiving the news. Philip spoke lovingly of their mother and urged Patrick to take care of her, which indeed he did throughout her long life.

At 17 he was out of work. The name Patrick Kay had appeared for the last time in *Fedora* at the Globe, in which he played a Russian page. His father was dying and his days were spent with his 'ballet mother' Astafieva, who encouraged and supported him in his passionate desire to dance. When his father died she also supported him financially by continuing to teach him for nothing. 'One day Patté will be a great dancer. Then he will pay.'

One September morning in 1921, the great Serge Diaghilev arrived at the studio, was embraced by Astafieva wearing, as always, a silk bandeau round her head, extremely high heels and ropes of pearls, and proceeded to audition some chosen pupils to perform as 'extras' in his large scale production of *The Sleeping Princess* at the Alhambra. Because it was the pantomime season the name had been changed from *The Sleeping Beauty* to avoid confusion. Marie Rambert always claimed that the suggestion was hers and no one ever disputed it.

There were three months of rehearsals at the army drill hall in Chenies Street, off Tottenham Court Road, an unforgettable period for the young dancer working with the renowned Russian régisseur, Nicolai Sergeyev, taking class with Bronislava Nijinska, sister of the dancer, and watching Olga Spessiva prepare for *Aurora*. 'Her dancing was an inspiration which has stayed with me all my life.'

Diaghilev had renamed Spessivtseva, Spessiva, and he decided Patrick Kay should become Patrikiev. Patrikiev was made a full member of the *corps de ballet* and partnered Lydia Sokolova (whose real name was Hilda Munnings) in the Act II *Waltz of the Flowers*. The production was enormously expensive, with real ermine on the costumes which made the dancers who had to wear them cry because they were so heavy and so hot. The Bakst décor was stunning but the mechanical scenery failed on the first night and the forest never grew to conceal the castle. After three months the losses were cut and the production closed. Before Diaghilev departed he asked Patrikiev 'And when will you dance the Blue Bird?' At that moment the prospect was glorious but unlikely.

With the Diaghilev company gone, the young dancer worked even more

Anton Dolin as Satan in Job.

energetically at his art. Astafieva arranged for him to take additional lessons with Nicholas Legat, the famous teacher of Nijinsky, recently arrived from Russia. He compared his new pupil to the statue of Eros in Piccadilly and it was in the north London church hall where he gave his lessons, that he introduced Patrick Kay to Anna Pavlova. 'You will one day be a good dancer', she said, and added that one day he might join her company.

Instead Diaghilev read the review of 'Anton Dolin' at the Albert Hall and wrote to Astafieva to ask who 'the young Russian' was. On learning it was Patrikiev, he arranged for an audition in Paris.

It is one of life's ironies that the very talented Joyce Berry who auditioned with Dolin, did not get a contract because Diaghilev thought she was his girlfriend. The impresario did not want any competition, and Dolin accepted the condition he felt was attached to his career. 'Though I was young and not too intelligent perhaps,' he wrote in his last memoirs, 'I realized no one but a fool would have refused.' He was an ambitious young man and Diaghilev and career 'were very much one' in his thoughts. He followed in the line of young protégés that included Nijinsky and Massine and concluded with Serge Lifar, who joined the company at the same time as Dolin but came into personal favour two years later.

Monte Carlo was a glamorous setting for the rich and famous. Gordon Selfridge, founder of the Oxford Street department store, escorted the brilliant musical-comedy Dolly sisters. Gossip columnist Elsa Maxwell, designer Coco Chanel and Francis Poulenc the composer all made the short journey from the Hotel de Paris to the Opera House to see the fashionable Ballets Russes. Presents were sent to the dancers, and an expensive wallet given to Dolin by an admirer was, on Diaghilev's order, returned.

During his initial months with the company, Dolin was in the *corps de ballet*, performing in *Prince Igor, Schéhérazade* and *Cléopâtre*. At the end of the year he was coached by Nijinska for the leading male role in *Daphnis and Chloe*, the first revival since Nijinsky had partnered Karsavina. There was a certain amount of hostility at Diaghilev's favouritism in the casting of Dolin. New solos and a *pas de deux* were choreographed by Nijinska, and Diaghilev invited Serafine Astafieva to attend the first night on the first day of the new year to see her ex-pupil dance his first major role with the Ballets Russes—incidentally the first Englishman to do so. Maurice Ravel conducted his own score, and Chloe was danced by Lydia Sokolova, who was to work with Dolin again in *Le Train Bleu*, a landmark for both the 21-year-old dancer and for the company.

It was certainly star-studded. The scenario was by Jean Cocteau, the costumes by Chanel, the choreography by Nijinska, the music by Darius Milhaud, the décor by Henri Laurens and the curtain designed by Picasso. The rather complicated scenario followed the pursuits of a group of chic, decadent young things on a Mediterranean beach, to which they had been transported by the express train of the title which ran between Paris and the *Côte d'Azur.*

The première was during the Paris summer season at the Theatre de Champs Elysèes. During rehearsals there was a surprise visit by the mentally afflicted Nijinsky, greatly affecting his sister, Nijinska, and everyone present. It was just one of the highly emotional incidents during the creation of the ballet. Changes to costumes and choreography occurred after heated and tense quarrels. Alterations were still being made 10 minutes before the curtain rose on Friday, 20 June 1924, and when it fell the audience rose to give a standing ovation to a work acclaimed as modern, witty and smart, and to Dolin's acrobatic bravura performance in his first created role.

The season ended and Diaghilev took his protégé off to Italy for a holiday, where they visited Milan, Florence and Venice. This was followed by a short German season, during which Dolin met Isadora Duncan. From Berlin the company travelled to London for a season at the Coliseum which opened with *Le Train Bleu.* Again there were complications; the scenery was too small for the stage; Dolin's part was extended. Again the audience was ecstatic, the press invoking the star's Dublin-born mother when they wrote rapturously of 'The Irishman in the Russian Ballet!' Later in the season he danced the Blue Bird variation from *The Sleeping Princess,* and Diaghilev remembered his words to Patrikiev two years earlier and sent him a laurel wreath—with a card which read: *Quand danserez-vous l'Oiseau Bleu? 1922-1924. SD.*

Back to Monte Carlo, and Dolin was partnering Vera Nemtchinova in *Lac des Cygnes* and Nijinska's house-party ballet, *Les Biches,* premièred the previous year. Nijinska left the company and was replaced by Massine; Lifar rose from the *corps,* and Dolin danced Nijinsky's *Spectre de la Rose.* The company visited Spain and then, as they had done the summer before, returned to London and the Coliseum.

Dolin had high hopes of repeating the excitement and success, but there were rows over the repertoire and personal conflicts, not least between Diaghilev and himself. Making his first entrance in *Les Biches,* Dolin trod on a nail which embedded itself into his toe. His contract was due to end in June and he felt increasingly that he had no desire to renew it. Gossip spread that it was out of jealousy because Diaghilev was now paying attention to Lifar. Dolin denied it. He had fallen in love with the brilliantly witty British comedy star Beatrice Lillie. When Cocteau knew that he was leaving, he declared that no one else would dance in *Le Train Bleu*. They never did. The ballet was dropped from the repertoire.

Dolin now had a spell in the commercial theatre, first in the long running review *The Punch Bowl* at His Majesty's Theatre in the Haymarket, where he joined the cast to dance his own arrangement of the popular song, *Alabamy Bound*, to which he added *The Hymn to the Sun* a few weeks later. This allowed him to buy his first car and a small house in South Kensington, and when the show closed he was engaged for a new revue, *Palladium Pleasures*, with a ballet to music by Vivian Ellis. After this not too successful venture, he appeared at the Coliseum with Phyllis Bedells, who became, many years later, Vice-President of the Royal Academy of Dancing after a distinguished dancing and teaching career.

Then came *The Chariot Revue of 1926*, *Piccadilly Revels*, and *Vaudeville Vanities*. He was making a comfortable living and enjoying celebrity life, and it was a satisfying linking of the two sides of his career when he appeared with Karsavina in *Spectre de la Rose* at the Coliseum, an exhausting two performances a day. The very expensive failure of *Whitebirds*, a show which involved Ninette de Valois and Maurice Chevalier among others and has its place in theatrical history, led Dolin back to ballet. His partner was Vera Nemchinova, with whom he had danced in the Ballets Russes. They had a successful and extended engagement at the Coliseum, followed by others in Paris, Nice, and Cannes, at the end of which they formed the Nemchinova-Dolin Ballet and accepted a season at the Champs-Elysées Theatre. For this season Dolin choreographed *Rhapsody in Blue* to the Gershwin music, a work that was popular at the time but not of lasting importance. The company danced in Strasbourg, Brussels, Amsterdam and Berlin as well as in a number of Italian cities on a tour which ended in financial loss. Nemchinova and Dolin were on tense terms by this time, and when Diaghilev approached him to dance again with the Ballets Russes, he was delighted to accept.

'Well, and so once more you will dance the Blue Bird!' Diaghilev's words ended their long estrangement, and Dolin was back in Monte Carlo rehearsing *Le Bal* choreographed by Georges Balanchine who was now the ballet master of the company. He did indeed dance the Blue Bird once more, and *Spectre de la Rose* with Alexandra Danilova.

It was a tremendous thrill for Dolin to return to London again with the Ballets Russes, this time at Covent Garden. If Lifar was the star of the season, Dolin received his share of plaudits, and audiences were especially pleased to watch the glittering performances of the Blue Bird *pas de deux* by two British artists,

Above *Anton Dolin as the Moor in London Festival Ballet's production of* Petrushka.

Left *Anton Dolin with Irina Baronova in Mikhail Fokine's ballet* Bluebeard *produced for (American) Ballet Theatre in 1941.*

Dolin and Markova. The season over, Dolin went with Balanchine and Lopokova to Isleworth studios outside London to dance in a film, *Dark Red Roses*. It was while waiting for the day's filming to begin that they learned of the death of Serge Diaghilev in Venice on 18 August 1929, a desolating shock, of which the journalist Hannen Swaffer wrote, 'The puppets had lost their master'. It was the end of an extraordinary and creative era.

On 8 January 1930, Dolin sailed for New York on the SS *Aquitania* to take part in *The International Revue* which turned out to be a theatrical nightmare for everyone involved. However, he spent time with his much loved Beatrice Lilley who was appearing at the Lido Club, and grew attached to the city where he was to live and work in later years. Just prior to leaving London, Dolin had been involved with the formation of the Carmargo Society which was to present ballet to subscription audiences. On his return he took part in the first perform-ance, on Sunday 19 October, dancing in Ashton's *Pomona* to music by Constant Lambert. Dolin and Anna Ludmila created the main roles in this one-act ballet, in which Walter Gore was Dolin's attendant, and Wendy Toye a nymph. At the end of the evening Lydia Lopokova told the audience they were assisting at the birth of British Ballet. Dolin could claim to have been one of the midwives.

The following year the Carmargo Society presented Ninette de Valois's *Job* at the Cambridge Theatre. Based on a scenario by Dr Geoffrey Keynes from Blake's *Vision of the Book of Job*, the theme was man's inward struggle between his inherent good and evil. Dolin danced Satan, with an unforgettable solo of superhuman arrogance and strength. The music was by Ralph Vaughan Williams, who in response to the enthusiastic applause, took part in a comic post-script to the evening, performing an inept *pas de deux* with Dolin amongst the angels displaying the wrong side of their wings.

The work went into the repertoire of the Vic-Wells Ballet on 9 September 1931, with Dolin repeating his success. For the next quarter of a century he was to dance Satan 30 times.

He continued with the Vic-Wells until 1935 when, with Alicia Markova, he left the company to form and direct the Markova-Dolin Ballet. At the outset, the repertoire was classical, with *Swan Lake*, *Nutcracker* and *Giselle*, but as the company became established modern works were introduced. Nijinska became ballet mistress and revived *Les Biches*, renamed *The House Party* for English audiences. Eighteen-year-old Wendy Toye choreographed her first ballet, *Aucassin and Nicolette*.

Dolin decided to recreate the *Pas de Quatre* designed in 1845 for four famous ballerinas of the day, Carlotta Grisi, Marie Taglioni, Fanny Cerrito and Lucile

Grahn. He owned a lithograph depicting them in the original production, and with little more to go on, commissioned Keith Lester to choreograph a new work with the right historical feeling. The Pugni music was discovered in the British Museum, and in May 1936 the ballet received its début at the Manchester Opera House with Molly Lake, Prudence Hyman, Kathleen Crofton and Diana Gould representing the renowned ballerinas. It was an immediate success.

Four years later, the Markova-Dolin Ballet disbanded and with England now at war, Dolin was in New York with the newly established American Ballet Theatre.* He was anxious to introduce *Pas de Quatre* into the repertoire, but Keith Lester's notes never arrived and so he decided to make a version of his own. Later it transpired that the notes were held by the War Customs authorities as being in some kind of code and a possible threat to safety. The code could have been deciphered by anyone familiar with ballet!

Dolin's *Pas de Quatre* was premièred in 1941 and was as well received as the Lester version had been. It remained in the repertoire and Markova, Nora Kaye and Alicia Alonso were among the distinguished ballerinas who danced it. It was filmed for British War Relief, with everyone giving their services free, but like the Lester notes, it disappeared and a valuable piece of dance history was lost to future generations.

Dolin's departure at the outset of war was not well received by his peers, but he states categorically that he volunteered for military service and was turned down because of his age. For five weeks he was in charge of an Air Raid Depot under the name of Patrick Kay and on a salary of £7.10s a week. No one told him what to do and he sat there bewildered until he decided to honour a commitment to dance in Australia with Colonel de Basil's company with which he had been appearing earlier in the year. He left on the last available ship, the SS *Washington*, met up with his partner Irina Baronova in New York and learned that she planned to stay in America. He did not want to go on to Australia without her and obtained a release from his contract. Lucia Chase invited him to stage *Swan Lake* Act II and *Giselle* for the company she had just founded. She was a lady with the determination, conviction and power of Diaghilev, and Dolin was to say that the survival of their friendship never ceased to amaze him. He was to dance with the American Ballet Theatre for the duration of the war.

He made his first real impact on American audiences with Fokine's *Bluebeard*, in which he created the title role. New York loved it, and so did the public on

* In 1957, the Ballet Theatre changed its name to the American Ballet Theatre. Throughout this book, the latter name has been used.

the annual coast-to-coast tours. The casts included Irina Baronova, Alicia Markova, Lucia Chase, Andre Eglevsky, Antony Tudor and Hugh Laing, who did much to establish the American Ballet Theatre throughout the world.

Dolin had met Igor Stravinsky during the 1921 Diaghilev *Sleeping Princess*, and in 1944 he worked with him in Hollywood on the score for *Scènes de Ballet*. Both had been commissioned by Billy Rose who wanted the ballet for his new show, *The Seven Lively Arts*. Rose had left the task of settling Stravinsky's fee to Dolin, who had the embarrassment of being the middle man in some tough negotiations. Altogether he did not enjoy his involvement with the show. It was generally hailed as being innovative and stylish, but Dolin had had difficulties with his choreography and was to say afterwards he found the whole enterprise pretentious and cheap. The only highlight had been working with his old friend Beatrice Lilley in a skit on the play *Gaslight*, but Lilley herself was recovering from the death of her son in action. It was not a happy period. Perhaps Dolin had been an expatriot long enough.

At the end of the war he and Markova decided to reform their company, and toured the United States and South America. They returned to Covent Garden as guests of Sadler's Wells Ballet for *Giselle* and *Swan Lake*. In 1948 Dolin revived *Pas de Quatre* for the *Ballets Russe de Monte Carlo* where it was a phenomenal success.

The following summer, already planning a new company with Alicia Markova and Dr Julian Braunsweg, Dolin went to Paris at the suggestion of Marie Rambert to see her pupil, John Gilpin, currently dancing there with the Marquis de Cuevas Ballet. Initially Dolin took a dislike to the brilliant, handsome young dancer, perhaps because some years before, when Gilpin was only 15, he had been heralded as 'the new Anton Dolin'. By the end of the year Gilpin had been engaged as the *premier danseur* of the about-to-be-launched Festival Ballet, and the friendship was established between the two men which was to last until the end of their lives. They were never lovers, although gossip continuously suggested it, but were the closest of companions. Once Marie Rambert accused Dolin of being 'a Diaghilev to my John Gilpin,' a remark Dolin said she regretted. 'For more than 30 years he was my friend, loyal, affectionate, and more than anyone understanding of my faults.'

Still called Pat by those who knew him well, Dolin had by this time legally changed his name to the one he had chosen so many years previously. In 1950 he procured the rights in the moral stage fable for children, *Where the Rainbow Ends* and not for the first time was playing St George at the Stoll Theatre where the Festival Ballet had made its debut on 24 October. With Dolin, Markova and Gilpin as its stars and a policy of inviting internationally famous guest artists, the company was launched with a programme of popular classics. Soon Dolin revived *Pas de Quatre* which became part of the repertoire and was performed regularly on the Festival's extensive tours at home and overseas. In 1952 Markova left the company, but Dolin continued as Artistic Director for another 10 years when Gilpin took over.

On his forty-ninth birthday, Dolin danced Albrecht in London. In April 1956 he was proud to be invited to take the Festival Ballet to Monte Carlo for the wedding celebrations of Prince Rainier and Grace Kelly. In 1960 his mother died, and he expressed the wish that, in due course, his ashes should be placed close to hers in the Brighton cemetery. For more than two decades, until that time came, he taught, travelled, directed and acted in America, France, Italy, Australia, and Great Britain. One of his last performances was as Oberon in Lindsay Kemp's idiosyncratic version of *A Midsummer Night's Dream*.

He was given a knighthood in the 1981 New Year's Honours List, and with Alicia Markova as his guest he attended the ceremony at Buckingham Palace. In July 1983 he was present at the Monte Carlo wedding of John Gilpin and Her Serene Highness, Princess Antoinette of Monaco, Prince Rainier's sister. Five weeks later John Gilpin died of a heart attack and Dolin was desolated. His own health suffered a set-back but within 10 weeks he made a planned journey to Paris, promising friends that he would see a doctor when he arrived. Tests were made and the doctor was able to tell him that all was well. As he was leaving with this reassuring news, he collapsed and lost consciousness and on 25 November 1983, his many friends and admirers throughout the world learned that Sir Anton Dolin was dead.

A·L·I·C·I·A M·A·R·K·O·V·A

Pavlova's advice to the very young Alicia Marks was that she should always take care of her teeth and rub herself down with cologne after dancing. By some miraculous diplomacy her father had achieved an audience for his daughter who was certainly under 10 years old, and there, in Pavlova's north London home, Ivy House, Alicia demonstrated her dancing abilities to her idol, a glorious vision in mauve.

Pavlova's name was to add prestige to Alicia's own when she was billed for her first professional appearance as Little Alicia, *The Child Pavlova* in Dick Whittington at the Kennington Theatre in 1920. When her mother subsequently presented the similarly printed calling card to the distinguished teacher, Princess Serafine Astafieva, she flew into a rage, shrieking that there was only *one* Pavlova, but fortunately she succumbed to Alicia's tears and auditioned her, an act on which they must have both looked back with gratitude.

Markova was born in Finsbury Park, north London, on 1 December 1910, to a girl from County Cork called Eileen, and a Jewish mining engineer with Polish forebears, Arthus, who longed for sons but sired four daughters. Alicia Lilian was the first, then came Doris, Vivien and Berenice who was known as Bunny. They were looked after by a lady called Gladys Hogan, nicknamed Guggy, who was a kind of nanny and governess rolled into one. Her mother was physically delicate and so was the child Alicia, succumbing to one complaint after another. It was what had been diagnosed as 'weak limbs' that prompted the first dancing lessons to strengthen them, at the Thorne Academy in Muswell Hill, and there she was taught all manner of fancy dancing including the swinging of Indian Clubs. Miss Thorne recognized talent, and soon Alicia was entering and winning dance competitions. It was at this point that she persuaded her adoring and adored father to take her to the Queen's Hall in Langham Place (bombed in 1941; St George's Hotel now stands on the site) to see Pavlova and dispatch a dubious Arthus backstage to importune a meeting.

Alicia's parents also took her to see Diaghilev's company, so when 'a very elegant gentleman' entered Astafieva's Chelsea studio, the 11-year-old student knew who he was. He had come talent-spotting and selected Patrick Healey Kay who was to be renamed Anton Dolin, and Alicia to dance the Fairy Dewdrop in his new production of *The Sleeping Princess*. The excitement was short-lived. Alicia caught diptheria and instead of performing at The Alhambra, she languished in an isolation hospital, buoyed up by a promise that if she worked hard she would have the chance of working with the company when she grew up.

Alicia Markova in Giselle, *first produced by Sadler's Wells Ballet in 1934.*

Before that, however, she was to perform with the Russian Art Dancers at The London Palladium, a group formed by one of the great Russian dancers and teachers, Nicholas Legat, and his wife, Nadine Nikolayeva. The engagement was part of a music-hall entertainment and Alicia, now 12, was once again selected from Astafieva's students. Dolin who used to pull Alicia's hair in class—was recruited as well for this tough season of two performances a night plus matinées, and some sort of truce must have been worked out, because when he joined the Diaghilev company they corresponded, relaying the Master's enquiries about her progress.

Alicia was deeply upset by the death of her father who had always been a support and comfort as well as a delightful companion, taking her to watch Arsenal as well as ballet performances. She worked harder than ever, rewarded one afternoon by an urgent telephone call from Astafieva's studio to go there at once, Diaghilev and Bronislav Nijinska wanted to see her dance. She had just eaten a substantial lunch, but no doubt the flow of adrenalin compensated, for after a two-hour audition she was designated a member of the Ballets Russes, to take up the appointment a month after her fourteenth birthday, the first (as she points out) of the famous 'baby ballerinas'.

It was an extraordinary period which followed. Diaghilev organized French lessons for his youngest company member, took her to museums and became a surrogate father figure. With Guggy to look after and chaperone her, preserving an element of normal life, she took class with Enrico Cecchetti, one of the greatest teachers in the history of the art. In *Le Rossignol*, the young George Balanchine choreographed her first role in his own creative Western début. There was an occasion in Paris when Matisse, the designer of the ballet, Stravinsky, its composer and Diaghilev supervised a costume fitting and fought over the cost of osprey feathers, with Matisse and Stravinsky eventually splitting the cost of her head-dress. With her in the company were Anton Dolin, Alexandra Danilova, Lydia Sokolova and Ninette de Valois, who took on the task of introducing Alicia to the world when Guggy suffered a mental breakdown and was no longer able to protect her charge. De Valois taught her how to budget and shop and order food in restaurants, and showed the artistic sights of Paris. Alicia greatly admired de Valois's chic clothes and hats and realized that Guggy had virtually isolated her from social contact and personal responsibility—she had even locked her in her hotel room when going to the post office in case disaster should strike. When Mrs Marks arrived to take over, de Valois's lessons were put to good effect, for it was Alicia's turn to be the guide and make the decisions for her mother, unused to being out of England.

At 16 Diaghilev demoted her from 'baby ballerina' with solo roles to the *corps de ballet*, a decision, she says, she has blessed ever since, learning the repertory the hard way, gradually working her way up again to soloist. Although by now she was adept at coping with the hazards of second-class travel and moving into an assortment of digs, she was still protected socially. Diaghilev would not allow her to accept invitations extended to the adult members of the company, or to take gifts from gentlemen admirers. Even chocolates had to be returned.

On her eighteenth birthday Diaghilev gave her her first glass of champagne and permission to attend functions for the company during the London season. She wore her first proper high-heeled shoes of silver kid and a Lanvin dress and at the end of the season Diaghilev told her she was to be promoted to principal and dance *Giselle*.

Just as diptheria had destroyed her hopes some years before, now an even greater disaster prevented her from dancing with the Ballets Russes. On 19 August 1929 the evening paper announced the devastating news with a stark headline— *Diaghilev Dead*. A letter from Serge Grigoriev, the company régisseur, followed with the inevitable statement that the Diaghilev era was over.

The young girl, on the brink of so much, felt she had lost not only inspiration, mentor and friend, but also her career. She thought she would never dance again and encouraged by her mother who pointed out that she was not pert and pretty enough for revue, she devoted herself to cooking and dress making. The depression which engulfed her was relieved by a letter from Frederick Ashton, whom she had never met, suggesting she might consider appearing with him in some dances he was arranging for a production of Dryden's *Mariage à la Mode* at the Lyric Theatre, Hammersmith. The fee was £10 (the same sum, incidentally, that she had received as the virtually untrained *Child Pavlova* in Dick Whittington which must say something about the state of the art!)

Ashton worked with Marie Rambert whose company was in the throes of being established with Ballet Club performances at the Mercury Theatre, Notting Hill Gate (owned by her husband, Ashley Dukes) and Markova was invited to join as guest ballerina. She appeared in the first of the Ballet Club evenings in *La Peri* which Ashton, inspired by an exhibition of Persian art, both choreographed and danced. *The Observer* reported that Markova 'danced divinely'.

In order to make financial ends meet, she danced between film shows at the Regal Cinema, Marble Arch, in rather more commercial Ashton works, in one piece descending on a crescent moon. On a Sunday night (her night off) she was able to perform with the Camargo Society, founded in 1930 to present ballet to subscription audiences, and she danced The Polka at the first performance of Ashton's comic masterpiece, *Facade*. The following year the young Antony Tudor at the beginning of his distinguished choreographic career, created the role of Myrrhina for her in his *Lysistrata*.

It was after one of these performances that Ninette de Valois approached Markova to join the Vic-Wells Ballet which was in its first year, and she now divided her time between Rambert's Ballet Club, the Camargo Society and the Vic-Wells as did many contemporary artists. She found the work intensely satisfying, staging *Les Sylphides* for de Valois as well as dancing in de Valois and Ashton works. Anton Dolin guested with the Vic-Wells partnering another Diaghilev dancer, Olga Spessivtseva in *Giselle*, both enthralling and poignant for Markova to watch, recalling the days in Monte Carlo with the Ballets Russes and the unfulfilled promise of dancing the role. One night Spessivtseva said to her, 'I hope that you have watched closely. This is a ballet that will be good for you.' Eighteen months later, by which time Markova was the prima ballerina of the company, she did at last dance *Giselle*. It was a night thick with London fog, the first day of 1934, and Giselle arrived at the theatre by tube, feeling her way along the Waterloo Road to the Old Vic stage door, wondering whether others would set out on such a hazardous journey, whether there would be an audience at all.

There was! An ecstatic audience who forgot the dank streets of the capital as they were drawn into a village in the Rhineland forest. With Dolin as Albrecht and Helpmann as his peasant rival Hilarion, that same night Ninette de Valois danced the peasant *pas de deux* with Stanley Judson; altogether a strong cast to support Markova in her historic début. She had been trained for the role by Nicholas Sergeyev who had brought from the Maryinsky Theatre thick ledgers containing the choreographic notation, teaching her in a way that was in perfect harmony with the music. Her first act was full of marvellous *joie de vivre*, culminating in despair as she died (not on the sword as in many versions) but of the physical anguish of a broken heart. 'I checked' writes Markova in her remembrances, 'and I was told that medically a victim of serious shock gradually becomes cold; the circulation is affected and the heart *can* stop.' In the second act in the cold moonlit forest, her physical presence was as light and aerial as if she really were an ethereal wraith. As it happened, some of the fog crept in under the doors and drifted on to the stage, nature adding an effect done nowadays with dry ice.

In personal terms the night was a landmark for the 23-year-old ballerina, enhanced by a present from Marie Rambert of the bodice worn by Karsarvina in the 1910 production. In general terms it was a landmark too for the Vic-Wells Ballet, as Ninette de Valois unveiled the first of the nineteenth-century ballets for the company that was to become England's Royal Ballet.

Sergeyev was to stage *Casse-Noisette*, with help from Lydia Lopokova, in which the greatest delight was Markova's glittering Sugar Plum Fairy. This he followed with *Lac des Cygnes* later anglicized as *Swan Lake* with Helpmann partnering Markova who had gone for extra coaching privately with Nicholas Legat. He had performed in the original 1895 version and taught her, she says, 'the secret' of the fabled Pierina Legnani's 32 fouettés.

Between these two classics came Ninette de Valois's *Haunted Ballroom*, with a romantic, melodic score by Geoffrey Toy and designed by a trio of talented women who together went under the name of Motley. The sets and costumes were in grey, white, black and gold, and Markova danced the principal ballerina role which was named after her, Alicia, and she was brilliantly fluent in the work's best choreography. At more or less the same time she was rehearsing another de Valois work, *Bar aux Folies Bergère* for the Ballet Club. This was based, needless to say, on the famous Manet painting, linked to the *louche* Paris of Toulouse-Lautrec. The scenario was written by Ashley Dukes for his wife's, Marie Rambert's, dancers and she took Markova to lunch in Soho on Saturday mornings after rehearsals to see the street prostitutes and learn their provocative style of walk. When Anton Dolin's mother saw the witty, stylish work she commented on Markova's 'roguish impertinence' and superb affrontery in her role of can-can dancer. 'You just won't know Alicia when you see her.'

The last season which Markova danced with the Vic-Wells was in 1935 when the company presented de Valois's masterpiece, *The Rake's Progress*, taken from the Hogarth paintings of the young Heir's descent from inheritance to debauchery, debt and death. The designs by Rex Whistler were brilliant evocations of Hogarth's work, perfectly distilled for theatrical effect. Gavin Gordon's score was dramatically apt for each of the scenes and characters, highlighting humour and tenderness and ruthlessness and madness with a sharp sense of period and place. As the Betrayed Girl Markova was poignantly lyrical. On the first night her Rake was Walter Gore, although Helpmann was to take over later. The season was extended commercially under the auspices of Vivian Van Damm who, with a Mrs Laura Henderson and Alicia Markova, formed the directorship of the Van Damm Productions, with Dolin under contract. Originally formulated to tour the Vic-Wells Ballet over the summer months, the company expanded to encompass the Markova-Dolin Ballet, and in Leeds on 7 September, the two dancers gave their farewell performance for de Valois and embarked on their own.

By November they were in Newcastle with 40 dancers and a repertory which included *Swan Lake* and *Nutcracker*, with *Giselle*, *Carnaval* and *Les Sylphides* in preparation. During the second season of this successful venture, Bronislava Nijinska became ballet mistress, and staged her ballet, *Les Biches*, under the new name of *The House Party*, and 18-year-old Wendy Toye produced her first ballet, *Aucassin and Nicolette*.

The company's London base was the Duke of York's Theatre and for two years appeared there between tours. Markova and Dolin danced leading roles for eight performances a week, and during one rehearsal period were to be seen in *Mother Goose* at the London Hippodrome! In 1937 the Markova-Dolin Ballet company was liquidated, with Markova joining Leonide Massine's new Ballet Russe de Monte Carlo and Dolin the rival Russian company under Colonel de Basil.

Massine invited Serge Lifar from the Paris Opéra to partner Markova in his own version of *Giselle*; which turned out to be heavily weighted in Albrecht's favour. At Drury Lane there were curtain-call tussles when the audience wanted Markova solo. Not much love was lost between the two artists, and the press came down on Markova's side. 'The performances' said the *News Chronicle*, 'ended with a campaign waged relentlessly by the gallery to separate Markova from her partner and give her her belated due.'

In 1939, and war very definitely on the horizon, Markova was in London ahead of the Monte Carlo company for a Covent Garden season. With Alexandra Danilova she decided not to stay with the Ballet Russe but to offer herself for war work, and when war was declared actually found employment washing-up and serving coffee to government workers in St John's Wood. This, however, did not suit Sol Hurok who had announced a season at the Metropolitan Opera House, and on legal advice, Danilova and Markova embarked on the SS *Manhattan* for New York, hoping that other members of the company would also find their way to the United States.

Artists arrived from all over Europe where they had been on holiday, and a mixed company of Ballet Russe dancers and Americans opened the season at the Met. Markova was adored by audiences there and in Rio, where the company went next. Warned of white slave traffic and the drinking-water, still suffering from vaccine fever and with the weather temperature at 100 degrees in the shade, she managed to dance *Swan Lake*. After the second night of *Giselle* she, Massine and Danilova joined the cast anonymously to compensate for those off sick, surely one of the most distinguished *corps de ballet* ever witnessed.

Markova was to stay in the United States for the duration of the war, giving her services at the Stage Door Canteen in New York, and in Bette Davis's Hollywood Canteen when she was in Los Angeles, performing for the wounded,

Above *Alicia Markova as Odile in* Swan Lake, *with Robert Helpmann as Prince Siegfried, in an early Sadler's Wells Ballet production.*

Right *Alicia Markova in* Haunted Ballroom, *a ballet by Ninette de Valois, first performed in 1934 by the Sadler's Wells Ballet.*

jitterbugging with the boys on leave. Travelling by bus for hours on end, living on special train coaches which pulled in long enough to set up and give performances, the glamour of the Ballet Russe was only in the eyes of the audiences. Markova recalls walking through the rattling train as the company hurtled across plains and deserts and seeing 48 pairs of pink silk tights hanging up to dry 'like a forest of legs'. There was a coach for the orchestra, two for crew and scenery and another for wardrobe, two for the dancers. She says they 'gypsied their way' across America, although Massine stayed aloof with caravan and chauffeured car.

In 1941, when Markova's Ballet Russe contract came to an end, she decided to join Lucia Chase's American Ballet Theatre. There she was among old friends, for Dolin, Massine and Antony Tudor were already committed to this new venture which Sol Hurok was promoting enthusiastically. A summer school at Jacob's Pillow in Massachusetts, where the venerated 'father' of American Dance, Ted Shawn, had lived and worked, kept the company solvent and together, and Markova rehearsed for the season ahead and organized the meals for the dancers and students.

Michel Fokine joined the American Ballet Theatre to produce, among other works, *Les Sylphides*. Fokine had split with Diaghilev before Markova became the 'first baby ballerina' in Monte Carlo, but she had danced several of his later works and the prospect of working with the Maestro had been one of the inducements to join the company. She did not find him personally charming but professionally it was a revelation. She imbibed 'every nuance of timing, phrasing, musical understanding'. He taught her to go beyond technique in this, the most difficult of ballets. 'Exits were not exits for you had to leave the stage as though you were reaching for the moon.' Fokine would shout, 'Reach, reach. The moon is up there!' Markova felt that although she had danced in *Les Sylphides* many times before, she had reached the very essence, the heart of the choreography.

Fokine's *Bluebeard* was created for the American Ballet Theatre, a comedy in which Markova was a Princess with Dolin as Bluebeard. The cast is worth recording for it included Rosella Hightower, Antony Tudor, Irina Baronova, Jerome Robbins, and Lucia Chase. More enthralling for Markova was *The Dying Swan*, which Fokine had choreographed for Pavlova thirty years before and now revived. The *Child Pavlova* had, in a sense, come of age.

Diaghilev had used important and distinguished artists to design his ballets—Matisse, Picasso, Bakst—and in the tradition Marc Chagall was invited to create the décor for the American Ballet Theatre's *Aleko* (based on Pushkin's poem,

Gypsies) and *The Firebird*. Markova's *Firebird* costume was strikingly dramatic, with bird of paradise feathers on the exotic head-dress, and gold dust gleaming on her back, shoulders and arms. She bought it, she says, by the pound, and her dresser used to throw it onto her grease-painted flesh. It took so long to soak off that there were many occasions when she dined and travelled with the sparkling make-up under a black cashmere sweater, waiting for the chance to take it off at last in the refuge of a hotel bedroom.

Today it seems extraordinary that a choreographer would turn down Prokoviev's score for *Romeo and Juliet*, but Fokine did, and then Antony Tudor, who decided on using music by Frederick Delius for his American Ballet Theatre production, together with décor by Salvador Dali which, not surprisingly, was unsuitable. Markova recalls a balcony devised as a set of dentures supported by crutches, rejected in favour of something romantic and traditional by Eugene Berman. The inspiration was Botticelli, and Markova chose to wear a ravishing auburn wig with the hair falling free, which gave her a look of impetuous youth. The management had billed her to dance Aurora on the matinée of opening night— too much even for a tough ballerina to cope with, and Nora Kaye made her début in the role that afternoon.

Markova's performance was sensitive and delicate and Tudor's one-act *Romeo and Juliet* was greatly admired, although inevitably the work has been overshadowed by the full length versions to the Prokoviev score.

Markova collapsed during a performance at the Hollywood Bowl and an operation for a hernia followed. It meant that American Ballet Theatre tours were too exhausting and she decided to do something very different—revue! At the newly refurbished Zeigfeld Theater she appeared with Anton Dolin in Billy Rose's *The Seven Lively Arts*. The show's premise was to present the finest in the contemporary theatre arts, and the billing included Beatrice Lillie, Bert Lahr and Benny Goodman. The music was by Cole Porter and, at Markova's suggestion, Igor Stravinsky who was commissioned by Rose to write something to reflect the spirit of Broadway. He produced *Scènes de Ballet*. Markova and Dolin collaborated on the choreography and Markova's first entrance down a long ramp opened the second half of the show which is now a part of theatre history. During the try-out in Philadelphia it was cut, but the full score of eleven 'numbers' was later choreographed and made famous by Frederick Ashton.

After the war a newly-formed Markova-Dolin Ballet toured not only the United States, but Mexico, Cuba and the Caribbean. In 1948, Markova and Dolin returned to England and Covent Garden to guest with Sadler's Wells Ballet. They danced *Giselle* and *Swan Lake* and Markova gave her first performance in the full-length *Sleeping Beauty*. For a year she and Dolin commuted between England and America, dancing in stadiums, theatres and concert halls, and in between going to Kenya, Rhodesia and South Africa. On the African tour Markova had to contend with the heart-breaking news that her much loved mother had died. Two years later, under the direction of Dr Julien Braunsweg, the British-Polish impresario, one-time manager of Pavlova, Markova and Dolin founded the Festival Ballet.

The new company was named by Alicia Markova after the Festival of Britain, which was the catalyst for new art styles and new perceptions and seemed to symbolize the end of austerity which had persisted since the end of the war. Visually and creatively the great Exhibition on the South Bank of the Thames flowered into a rebirth of the arts, and Festival Ballet was an enduring pinnacle. With a *corps de ballet* and soloists, all graduates from the Arts Educational School (which still supplies dancers and the children for the annual *Nutcracker*) and glittering guest stars—Leonide Massine, David Lichine and his wife Tatiana Riabouchinska—Festival Ballet reached London's Stoll Theatre in the autumn of 1950. It aimed at box-office appeal with popular classics and famous guests, creating its own stars like John Gilpin who took over as Artistic Director in 1962. With extensive tours and London seasons at the Festival Hall, the Coliseum and the New Victoria under Beryl Grey, John Field and now Peter Schaufuss, the company has an established place in British ballet and a world audience.

Markova left Festival after two years, although she still guested with them between appearances with American Ballet Theatre, the Royal Danish Ballet, the Grand Ballet du Marquis de Cuevas, Chicago Ballet and the Royal Ballet, a hectic schedule she was to continue for the next 10 years. On the first day of January 1963 she was on her way to New York with the usual press coverage, when a journalist asked her if she had any New Year resolutions. Yes, she said on impulse, she was retiring. Suddenly, at 52, she had made her decision. Her last performance with Festival Ballet was, in fact, her last performance. By the time her plane landed in New York she had made headlines on both sides of the Atlantic.

Alicia Markova has retired only from dancing. She spent six years as a director of the Opera Ballet at the Met, New York, then returned to Britain to be a Governor of the Royal Ballet, Vice-President of the Royal Academy of Dancing and President of the Arts Educational Trust. She teaches and coaches and is constantly involved with all aspects of her art. In looking back over her full and varied career and the great partnership with Dolin, one is aware of another, more private partnership with her sister, Doris Barry, working with her and alongside her and providing the emotional equivalent of a balletic lift.

Alicia Markova was awarded the CBE in 1958 and was made a Dame of the British Empire in 1963.

S·E·R·G·E L·I·F·A·R

Serge Lifar was the last of a succession of great *premiers danseurs* who were protégés of Diaghilev, but his subsequent career as dancer, ballet-master and Director of the Paris Opera Ballet proved even more important in an era when ballet itself was developing its potency as a highly expressive form of theatre.

Lifar became a dancer almost by chance. He was born in the great early-Christian Ukrainian city of Kiev on 2 April 1905—the year of the first, abortive uprising against Tsar Nicholas II. Lifar had two elder brothers, Vassili and Leonide, and an elder sister, Eugenia. His father was a civil servant in the Department of Waterways and Forests. Born into the culturally aware bourgeoisie, in which theatre, opera and music were an accepted part of civilized life, his childhood and adolescence were marked by violent national and international turbulence which, amongst other things, disrupted his studies at the University. He was nine years old when World War I began and the family home was threatened by the advancing German armies. The Russian revolution took place in 1917, but it was another year before the Bolsheviks, under Lenin, signed an armistice with the Germans, during which time they had occupied Kiev and Lifar's grandmother was burnt alive in her home.

But with the armistice signed between the Germans and Russians, Lifar was caught up in the fighting between his own factional countrymen. Kiev was one of the strongholds of the White Russians fighting the Reds (Bolsheviks) and at first the adolescent Lifar was drafted into the White Russian forces. Murder, looting, death, and destruction overtook the city which was occupied by various forces no fewer than 18 times. Famine and disease followed in the wake of war and revolution. Lifar, together with his father and brother Vassili, having been in the White Army, took refuge for a while in the surrounding forests, living a hand-to-mouth existence. One evening, in a small township, Lifar saw a detachment of Red soldiers performing a series of lively folk-dances which entranced him. Returning to the city he was drafted into the Red Army. One day he was wandering aimlessly in the city with a comrade who casually suggested they enter the studio of Bronislava Nijinska who, soon after the revolution, had set up her school of dance in the city and who was ballet mistress of the Kiev Opera.

The order and discipline of the studio, together with the music of Schumann and Chopin, were in vivid contrast to the anarchy and chaos in the streets and for the impressionable young soldier—he was still only 15—it was a revelation. Next day he returned and asked to join Nijinska's school. 'She refused to have

Serge Lifar on holiday in Venice with Serge Diaghilev (foreground) and Walter Nouvel, one of Diaghilev's earliest collaborators and loyal friends.

me. Her voice was harsh and her words few,' he later wrote. But he was advised
to apply to Comrade Steiman, Director of the Opera who was an influential figure
looked upon with favour by the Soviet authorities. Steiman arranged for Lifar
to study at the State Ballet School, amongst an oddly assorted crowd of refugee
villagers, young workmen, dispossessed intellectuals—hardly the sort of ballet
students who would have been accepted into the Imperial Ballet School at St
Petersburg.

Nijinska's report at his audition wrote the one devastating word 'hunchback'
against his name which prompted Lifar to present a medical report attesting
that he stood perfectly upright. Lifar worked hard at the school but Nijinska
refused to take notice of him—she was obviously irked that her initial refusal
to have him as a pupil had been circumvented. Nevertheless he respected, even
venerated her as a teacher. Then, suddenly, Nijinska left the school, having
managed to 'flee from the Soviet yoke' and rejoin Diaghilev in the West as dancer
and choreographer.

For the next 15 months Lifar worked hard at the school although he had
no teacher of consequence, only a senior pupil of Nijinska. Then one day a
telegram arrived at the school—a telegram which, in its shattering import, Lifar
had the foresight to keep. It said: *S.P. Diaghilev asks for Mme Nijinska's five
best pupils to complete his troupe.* The five were chosen; the fifth did not turn
up but Lifar was so enthusiastic 'I managed to carry the day for myself'. The
only person he told was his mother, who blessed him. He never saw her again.

On 13 January 1923, he was in Paris, inspected by Diaghilev at the Hotel
Continental. Diaghilev said very little, except to tell the new recruits that their
salaries would be considerably less than they had been promised. But next day
they were on their way to Monte Carlo where the sunshine, the flowers, the elegant
buildings, the glittering Mediterranean seemed like paradise after the cold and
chaos of Soviet Russia. After three weeks Diaghilev arrived and asked to see
the newcomers. Within minutes he had stormed out, bawling at Nijinska 'Crass
ignorance . . . you've fooled me . . . let them return to Russia!' But he was calmed
down and returned to see the second half of the class, at the end of which he
murmured in Lifar's direction, 'He'll be a dancer'. Those words carried as much
import as the telegram had done.

So Lifar stayed on, working and studying assiduously, constantly aware of his
lowly status in a company in which all the dancers were strict in their observance
of hierarchy. Even so, by small degrees, by an occasional, casual word of praise,
Diaghilev intimated that he was watching the young man's progress, that he had
hopes for him. Even a reprimand could be interpreted as something favourable;

the mere fact of being noticed carried intimations of future glory.

The first ballet in which Lifar appeared was Nijinska's *Les Noces*, an innovative work, based on a study of a Russian peasant wedding, with a score by Stravinsky subsequently hailed as one of the masterpieces of the century. The ballet used the *corps* in a monumental manner, with big blocks of dancers moving in unison, performing steps based on peasant dances, a complex counterpoint to Stravinsky's equally complicated cross-rhythms. Classical style was jettisoned except for a few females who danced on *pointe*. Lifar's performance brought forth one of Diaghilev's rare utterances of praise: 'Very good, young man, go on like that, work in the right way', though what 'the right way' might be he did not elucidate. Later he suggested to Nijinska that Lifar might be given a minor role but she, still prejudiced against the young man, objected.

While the company was in Paris, Lifar rented a small room in the red light district. Unable to practise in his tiny attic he worked on the pavement, encouraged by the bravos from the ladies of the evening who watched from their upper windows. During that Paris season Lifar appeared in the *Polovtsian Dances* from *Prince Igor* and in *Petrouchka* in which he played the tiny character role of an urchin in the fairground scenes and was complimented on his performance by Alexandre Benois, the designer of the ballet, and one of the inspirational forces behind its conception.

In *Schéhérazade*, however, he was taken to task by Diaghilev himself for his over-enthusiastic death scene as one of the slaves, a brief moment when, instead of just falling to the ground he made a spectacular roll down a flight of steps. This earned him a lecture about self-discipline and distracting the audience's attention from the main action but, once again, he was pleased to have come to the attention of the all-powerful impresario.

This attention, of course, was not entirely to do with aesthetics. Diaghilev's penchant for attractive young men, his past associations with Nijinsky and Massine were common knowledge, at least amongst the company, and to quote Lifar's own words, 'At nineteen years of age one would have to be devoid both of intuition and sensitiveness not to have an inkling of power possessed, of charm exercised— and I did not lack the one or the other.' This 'intuition' was considerably reinforced when Diaghilev asked Lifar to have himself photographed in his costume as an officer in Nijinska's latest ballet, *Les Fâcheux*, based on Molière's play and which had a décor by Georges Braque. This small role was Lifar's first created part; he subsequently discovered that Diaghilev had kept three of the photographs for his private collection, Lifar also noticed, with considerable satisfaction that, aware of Diaghilev's growing interest in him, his confrères had also begun to pay him greater attention—even some of the more illustrious members of the company and Diaghilev's personal entourage.

A few days after the première of *Le Train Bleu*, Jean Cocteau's chic ballet which had costumes by Coco Chanel and a famous front-cloth by Picasso, and in which Anton Dolin scored a major success, Lifar asked for a meeting with Diaghilev. They were having tea together when Lifar announced he was leaving the company. In a towering rage Diaghilev upset the tea-table with a crash of china. When it had been restored Lifar went on to explain that, because of his doubts about his future as a dancer, he was going to enter a monastery. Diaghilev then lay his large head upon the table, sobbing. Recovering, he assured Lifar that he had the highest hopes of him, that he would be a *premier danseur*, that were it not for Lifar he would have disbanded the company. Lifar then suggested that he should take lessons in Turin with the great teacher Enrico Cecchetti who had coached Nijinsky and Karsavina, Fokine and Massine. Diaghilev leapt to his feet, saying the idea was 'a stroke of genius'. He fitted Lifar out with new clothes, with books, and personally obtained Lifar's Italian visa from Mussolini, dictator of the new Fascist state.

One cannot help wondering if this extraordinary scene and its outcome was not the result of a young man who was very much aware of 'the power possessed, of charm exercised'. If so it was astutely and adroitly exercised.

When Diaghilev told Nijinska he was sending Lifar to take lessons with Cecchetti she was 'much annoyed' and wagered Diaghilev that Lifar would never become a *premier danseur*—or even a soloist. She lost the bet—a case of champagne—but Diaghilev never got his wine. By the time Lifar had been promoted to *premier danseur* she had left the company.

Lifar's sojourn with Cecchetti was a lonely and laborious one: three hours work a day—Cecchetti was a martinet who carried a stick with which to hit his pupils—followed by long, dreary hours in his small room. He read the books Diaghilev had given him, then one day received a note saying he should meet the impresario in Milan. Diaghilev intended that, as with Nijinsky and Massine, he would be responsible for Lifar's artistic education with visits to galleries, churches and museums. In Milan they visited the cathedral, the Victor Emmanuel Gallery, the church of Santa Maria della Grazia with Leonardo da Vinci's painting of the *Last Supper*. After Diaghilev had gone and Lifar was back in Turin with Cecchetti, he wrote a rather naive letter to the impresario expounding his feelings of inadequacy. We may suppose that he felt he had been 'inadequate' both as an intellectual companion and as the lover he was obviously expected to be.

Diaghilev's disgruntled reply spoke of the need for a 'real artist' to appreciate the 'beautiful things the world contains'. It also mentioned his displeasure at 'unfinished expressions which are perfectly useless'. The letter went on to say that Lifar would be receiving a surprise package. Immediately he imagined some elegant gift: 'ties? Some knick-knacks? Something to help me relax after my hard work with Cecchetti?' His rather gigolo-ish expectations turned to disappointed annoyance when the package proved to contain pamphlets of reproductions of paintings by famous artists. Lifar felt he was being made a fool of.

After a long silence Diaghilev sent another letter telling him to settle up with Cecchetti and meet him in Milan. From there they spent an idyllic holiday in Venice, Diaghilev's favourite city where, like Nijinsky and Massine before him, Lifar was shown the splendours of its palaces and introduced to the pleasures of its elegant society. Diaghilev also confided that he was sure Lifar would soon prove to be the new choreographer of the Ballets Russes. At that moment, Lifar later wrote in his autobiography, 'there sparked in me an urge to create that has never since left me'.

When the new season began in Paris that autumn everyone, including Diaghilev, was amazed at the progress Lifar had made studying with Cecchetti. After a long tour of Germany the company arrived in London where Diaghilev planned to première a new ballet, *Zephyr et Flore*, to be choreographed by Nijinska. She, however, was piqued at Diaghilev's decision to give the leading role to Lifar, and after a row left the company. Diaghilev announced that Lifar would take over the choreography. After some sleepless nights contemplating the responsibility laid upon him, Lifar proposed to Diaghilev that he should entrust the work to Massine, with whom he was once again on good terms. Diaghilev was furious at Lifar's suggestion, but Massine did choreograph the work and Lifar always felt he had made a wise decision not to make a precipitate début as a choreographer. At the end of the Paris season the following year Anton Dolin left the company and Lifar, who had scored successes in *Zephyr et Flore* and in another Massine ballet, *Les Matelots*, with music by Georges Auric and scenario by Boris Kochno, was named as *premier danseur*. Diaghilev's prognostication had come true.

For the Paris season of 1929 Lifar undertook his first choreography, a revival of Stravinsky's *Le Renard*, a Russian fable, first choreographed by Nijinska in 1922. It was given its première at the same time as Balanchine's *The Prodigal Son*—Lifar had scored a personal success the year before in Balanchine's neoclassic *Apollon Musagete*, later retitled, simply, *Apollo*, one of the masterpieces of this century. In his autobiography, *Ma Vie*, Lifar refers to *Le Renard* as 'a triumph'. He goes on to infer that *The Prodigal Son* was also a triumph—but only because of his performance in the title role which he 'improvized, as it were in a nightmare'. It is hardly credible that Balanchine would permit a dancer to *improvize* a role—unless, of course, Lifar had not bothered to learn it. At any rate, Lifar's ballet has sunk without trace while Balanchine's is in the repertoire of several companies throughout the world and is regularly performed to this day.

After the Paris season the company visited London, followed by a long tour of Germany. During this time Lifar saw little of Diaghilev who spent much time in the company of the 16-year-old Igor Markevitch, who later became a distinguished conductor. In August Lifar visited Diaghilev in Venice, where he was staying at the Hotel des Bains on the Lido. His intention was to inform Diaghilev of his decision to resign from the Ballets Russes, but when he saw how ill Diaghilev looked he said nothing. Within 10 days Diaghilev was dead, and with him the great company with which he had astonished the Western world for 20 years, employing all the greatest artists, writers and musicians of the time as his collaborators, and presenting the greatest assembly of dancers the world has ever seen.

Following the funeral in Venice Lifar spent a short while in Toulon 'in solitary meditation', and then hurried to Paris where, in company with Paul Koriboute, a member of Diaghilev's staff, Walter Nouvel, his manager and Boris Kochno, his secretary, he effected an entry to Diaghilev's apartment in the Boulevard Garibaldi and carried away numerous *objets*, scores, manuscripts, rare books, pictures and important memorabilia which would otherwise have been 'put up for sale'.

Almost immediately after Diaghilev's death Lifar received offers to dance with the Paris Opera Ballet, with Pavlova's company and from Charles B. Cochran in London; he settled for the Paris Opera where he was to reign supreme for nearly 30 years.

He was engaged as *premier danseur*, choreographer and ballet-master, and his first work was the revival of Beethoven's only ballet, *The Creatures of Prometheus*, a work which had never had much success, from the very first production by Salvatore Vigano in Vienna, 1801. Knowing this, Lifar very astutely suggested that it might be better if the management engaged Balanchine to create the choreography, but Balanchine became ill after only a week or two after beginning work on the ballet and Lifar was prevailed upon to take over. He engaged the great Russian ballerina Olga Spessivtseva (aka Spessiva) who had been a guest artist with Diaghilev, to dance one of the main roles and, with himself in the title role, the ballet achieved a certain success. As a result he was offered a permanent contract as Director of the Opera Ballet.

Right Serge Lifar in Salade, a ballet with a Commedia dell'arte theme.

Below Serge Lifar in the title role of his ballet Icare.

At the time he took over control of the great French company he was arguably the greatest male dancer of his generation, and his position as Director gave him enormous power. But the company itself was in poor shape, the dancers possessed of only indifferent technique, and without a corporate sense of purpose or commitment. Yet at the same time as he was involved with Paris he also took up a contract to dance in Cochran's show, so that he became an early commuter by air between Paris and London, where he bought expensive suits from Savile Row and was involved in a round of parties, receptions and balls. He received an offer from Leopold Stokowski to direct ballets at the Metropolitan Opera in New York but the Paris Opera remained, as he put it, 'a beacon before my eyes'. Prudently, he turned down another offer, this time from Stalin, via Sokolnikov, the Soviet ambassador in London, to direct a company in his native Russia. He felt that, as a professed White Russian, the Soviet authorities would not be so friendly once he was behind the frontier.

He was fêted by London society, was taken to Buckingham Palace by the Duke of Kent and his friends 'until King George [V] asked us to go and indulge in our gaiety elsewhere'. He also received an offer of marriage which he turned down, from a mysterious Lady F.

Back in Paris he began, methodically, to reorganize and revitalize the Opera Ballet. As a new broom he had to sweep away many of the traditions that had grown up over the years, such as the well-connected gentlemen who, as subscribers to the opera season, were also allowed to attend rehearsals in the famous *foyer de la danse* which they used as a sort of club in which they made assignations with the young women of the *corps de ballet*. Lifar overcame this difficulty by cleverly arranging for a number of the soloists to take lessons with the great Russian teachers, ex-dancers from the Imperial Ballet in St Petersburg, such as Lubov Egorova, Vera Trefilova, Olga Preobrajenska and Mathilde Kschessinska. There was, of course, much opposition to his measures, but he had the powerful and loyal support of Jacques Rouché, Director of the Opera who had appointed him, and the several plots to have Lifar ousted were defeated.

Even so, his artistic policies met a good deal of opposition from the regular opera audience which had not assimilated the aesthetic revolution in dance achieved by Diaghilev's Ballets Russes. Lifar's next major production, *Bacchus and Ariadne*, with music by Albert Roussel and décor by the metaphysical painter Giorgio de Chirico, provoked catcalls and boos, reminiscent of the reception afforded Nijinsky's *Rite of Spring* in 1913. But this was 1931, and the noisy reception was rooted more in politics than aesthetics. Politics were partly to blame for the reconsideration of the season for 1931-32. Rouché told Lifar there was very little money available for 'experimentation', that they would have to devise some programmes that would cost little and provide good box-office returns. Lifar, sensing that discretion was advisable at this point proposed reviving tried favourites such as *Giselle*, the *divertissements* from the last act of *The Sleeping Beauty* and a revival of Fokine's *Spectre of the Rose*.

Both *Spectre of the Rose* and *Giselle*, with Lifar partnering Spessivtseva, were immensely successful with the Parisian public and his enemies were, for the time being, unable to say that he was 'destroying the heritage of French ballet'. The important critic André Levinson compared the dancing of the two principals in *Giselle* with that of Nijinsky and Karsavina in 1910.

At the age of 30 Lifar wrote a rather pretentious and obscure manifesto about the art of ballet in which he proclaimed it should be free from the yoke of music—if necessary all musical accompaniment. Of course it provoked a lot of heated discussion and Lifar himself did little to heed his own aesthetic credo. The one work which did dispense with music and was performed to a percussive accompaniment devised by Honegger, was *Icare*. Based on the Greek legend (Lifar had just spent a holiday in Greece) of Icarus who attempting to fly with a pair of wings made by his father Daedelus, flew too near the sun which melted his wings so that he crashed to earth, the ballet was really a long virtuoso solo, performed by Lifar, with an accompanying group. Lifar commissioned a décor from the surrealist painter Salvador Dali but the model which Dali submitted 'could not possibly be considered'. The design was ultimately carried out by P. R. Larthe. After several postponements the first performance finally took place on 9 July 1935. It was a great success and proved a personal triumph for Lifar. The work has often been revived and was given a new décor by Picasso in 1962.

Throughout the last years of the thirties, as Europe marched inexorably towards war, Lifar continued to direct the Paris Opera Ballet with growing authority, building a splendid company of principals, soloists and *corps de ballet* and instituting a superb curriculum of training—a foundation which has, to this day, maintained the technical excellence of the company. Throughout this period Lifar continued to create a flow of new works for the company, including *Harnasie*, dealing with the legendary robbers of the Tatra mountains, and first produced for the National Theatre of Prague, with music by Karol Szymanowski and produced for the Paris Opera Ballet in 1936; *Le Roi nu* (The Emperor's New Clothes), to music by Jean Francaix; *Alexander the Great*, with music by Philippe Gaubert and *Oriane et le Prince d'amour*, to music by Florent Schmitt. All these works provided leading roles for Lifar himself and added new laurels to his reputation as one of the greatest male dancers in the world at that time.

As well as his successful control of the Paris Opera Ballet, Lifar revelled in meeting powerful and influential people: in the governments of the day, in the diplomatic corps, in the arts, in the aristocracy, and the rich and famous in society. He was friendly with the Duke and Duchess of Windsor, he was received by Mussolini and Prince Umberto, and he was given an inscribed gold cigarette case from King George VI and Queen Elizabeth after he had danced before them at the Opera during their state visit in 1938.

When war broke out in 1939 the opera house was closed. Lifar managed to arrange a visit to Australia, dancing with an *ad hoc* company put together by Colonel de Basil, but the trip turned out to be something of a fiasco, although Lifar claimed to have 'saved the whole enterprise', by his performances in *Icare* and the Bluebird *pas de deux*.

Returning to Paris via Naples, where he met and talked with Count Ciano, Mussolini's son-in-law and Foreign Minister, Lifar produced two further works, *Entre deux rondes*, to music by M. Samuel Rosseau, and *Le Chevalier et la demoiselle*, which had a score by Philippe Gaubert who was the new Director of the Opera. Just as the Western Front began to collapse and the German Panzer divisions broke through, Lifar led the Opera Ballet on a tour to Spain. By the time they returned to Paris the government had fled, Marshall Pétain had taken over what was to be known as the collaborative Vichy government and everything was in chaos, with Nazi troops occupying the capital.

At first the Opera was closed. Lifar was summoned to the Hotel de Ville where he was met by the Prefect of Police and a deputation of Ministers who placed him in continuing charge of the Paris Opera Ballet. Lifar accepted the position, knowing full well that he would have to negotiate with the German occupying authorities.

Throughout the war Lifar remained as Director of the Paris Opera Ballet. In this position he received Hitler's Minister for Propaganda, Dr Goebbels, and Reichsmarschall Hermann Goering, Commander of the *Luftwaffe*; he danced at a special reception for General von Brauchitsch, chief of the German General Staff; he visited Marshall Pétain in Vichy, who put a car at his disposal for a holiday in the South of France; he was invited to Berlin where he met Hitler; he was sculpted by Arno Breker, official artist to the Nazi regime—in short, he was seen to be in direct collaboration with the Nazi government and its despised puppet regime in Vichy. For this, after the Allied liberation of Paris, he was arraigned by a French Resistance court and sentenced to 'exclusion for life from the Opera and from State theatres'.

But Lifar's balletic activities did not stop. In 1944 he took refuge from his own reputation with friends in Bordeaux. In 1945 he was invited to direct the Nouveau Ballet de Monte Carlo. For this company he created a number of works, including *Dramma per musica*, to a cantata by Bach; *Chota Roustavelli*, a four-act work about the Georgian poet and his love for Queen Thamar, using music by Arthur Honegger, Nicholai Tcherepnin, and Tibor Harsanyi; *La Peri*, to the score by Paul Dukas, and *Salome*, to the music from the opera by Richard Strauss. The company later toured Italy and Switzerland and then appeared at the Cambridge Theatre in London with some success, although a gala, at which Queen Elizabeth was invited to appear, was cancelled.

In October 1945, Lifar was once more called before a 'purge committee'. In consideration of the fact that he had not been convicted by a formally convened French Court of Justice he was asked to accept 'a leave of absence for one year'. Thus, from 1 November 1945, he was free to return to the Paris Opera Ballet. His contract was renewed and, although there was a certain amount of hostility at his return, he created a number of new works for the company, the most important of which was *Phédre*, with music by Georges Auric, a scenario by Jean Cocteau and décor by Christian Bérard.

Lifar's last performance was as Albrecht in *Giselle*, on 5 December 1956, a role he cherished 'above all others'. From his large output, few works have remained in the repertoires of the companies for which he created them, many of them now having rather a dated look. Of those that are still performed, *Suite en Blanc* (sometimes retitled *Noir et Blanc*) to music by Edouard Lalo, is probably the best. It is a spectacular display piece for a large company in Lifar's grandiloquent style, a ballet demanding tremendous technical security and virtuosity if it is to be seen to advantage. It entered the repertoire of London Festival Ballet in 1966 and has been irregularly revived ever since.

Few dancers can have had such a colourful career as Lifar. It began in turmoil and continued in the same manner throughout his life, in his emotional entanglements with Diaghilev and a succession of lovers of both sexes, in his artistic wrangles, in his political involvements which were not so much from any ideological convictions as, perhaps, in having 'an eye to the main chance'. What is indisputable is that he was a superb dancer and he was instrumental in re-establishing the Paris Opera Ballet to its position as one of the great companies in the world today.

Lifar died in Lausanne on 15 December 1986.

G·A·L·I·N·A U·L·A·N·O·V·A

Galina Ulanova was 46 when London audiences saw her dance for the first time and compared her to Margot Fonteyn. Fonteyn was nine years her junior but both ballerinas held—indeed still hold in their retirement—what can only be described as a cherished place in the hearts and minds of the public. Like Shakespeare's Cleopatra 'age did not wither' them and while their physical abilities inevitably declined, they brought extraordinary qualities to certain roles that remained paramount in the memories of those who had seen them.

Fonteyn, of course, had the opportunities of a far greater repertoire. Ulanova is associated with Giselle and Juliet in particular, and it was her Juliet that astonished ballet-goers when the Bolshoi came to Britain in 1956. Even more astonished were the people who saw her off-stage. The radiant teenager turned out to be definitely in her fifth decade, with short neck and arms and rather broad shoulders, unassuming and completely without glamour. The unmatchable lyricism, expressiveness, and romanticism were completely at odds with the rather dowdy and unforthcoming woman.

By the time she came to the West, Ulanova could almost be described as a state monument in her native Russia. She had been idolized throughout the Stalin years, by chance rather than design, conforming to the ideological concept of Soviet womanhood. As with all totalitarian regimes, the stereotyped image was simple, strong, unadorned, capable of child-bearing and home-making, submissive to the role demanded by the state. Ulanova's lack of sensuality and sexuality in her art perfectly fitted the official image, and in the chicken-and-egg situation, audiences responded to her. She inadvertantly furthered Communist propaganda because she was the dancer she happened to be. She was anything but the threatening *femme fatale*. Those who found her appeal negative secretly accused her of dancing an 'eternal *valse triste*'. All she wanted to do was to devote herself to her dancing.

Her parents were both dancers of the Maryinsky (now the Kirov) company, although her father retired to become a stage manager of the company when she was nine. Sergei Ulanov was an undemonstrative and taciturn man, but for his daughter he symbolized honour and devotion to both his family and the theatre. Her passive approach to politics is mirrored by her parents' determination

Apart from her memorable performances as Juliet, Ulanova astonished London audiences with the delicacy of her dancing and the dramatic power of her acting in Giselle, *when the Bolshoi Ballet first came to Britain in 1956. In this picture she is partnered by Nicolai Fadeyechev as Albrecht.*

to pursue their profession despite the revolution, although she phrased this in a way demanded by the editors of *Soviet Weekly*: 'I am proud that my parents were among those people of the arts who resolved from the very beginning to devote their art to the revolution.' In other words, they had no intention of rocking the boat!

Mother was Maria Romanova who danced the Lilac Fairy in *The Sleeping Beauty* and Galina was four years old when she first saw her dance. 'Look, that's Mummy!' she called out to the amused embarrassment of her father and grandmother. She had suddenly discovered, she said, that magic is real, and the beautiful fairy was her own adored mother, and adoration is not too strong a word for the intense love and admiration she felt not only then but throughout her life. 'To speak of one's mother is always both easy and difficult. It is easy because one's earliest and warmest memories of life are bound up with her . . . but it is difficult to speak of her because she means so much to you.' In this case not only was her mother the source of comfort and pleasure but also her teacher, 'the finest example I had before me in my profession . . . the greatest authority I knew on the ballet.'

It was the example of her parents that made the child aware of the hard work involved. Long before she herself entered ballet school she knew that daily class was essential, that there was exhaustion and sometimes pain and injury in order to present to the audience an impression of effortless ease. In addition to the dancer's unremitting training, in Petrograd as it was still called in 1918, personal endurance required an equal measure of stamina. This was the city where the revolution had begun and the new order was not yet established. Shortages of all kinds brought fresh problems daily, but at least the violent social upheaval did not involve artists of the ballet who stayed clear of politics. In fact there was a movement to bring the great stage artists before the workers, and one of the methods devised was to have them perform between film performances in the cinema.

When they were not dancing at the Maryinsky, Maria and Sergei crossed the city on foot because the trams were not running. They took Galina with them, and she sat with her mother in a room the size of a cupboard behind the screen. The iron stove melted the snow from their felt boots, and with frozen fingers Maria put on her *pointe* shoes and tutu and, when the film ended, she went out onto the tiny stage to dance.

The cinema auditorium was unheated but the reception for the singers and dancers was warm. When the live acts were over, the artists retired backstage until the next interval, but by this time Galina was usually asleep and her father carried her home through the snow-covered streets. At home Maria began the domestic chores she had no time for during the day. If Galina woke in the night she always recalled seeing her mother mending or making clothes, washing them, or hanging them up to dry. Not surprisingly the child quailed at the prospect of a dancing career when her parents began to discuss it. She thought she wouldn't have enough sleep!

In 1919, the year her father gave up dancing, Galina became a boarder at the Leningrad State Choreographic School attached to the theatre, but she did not lose parental contact during the term time because it was her mother who taught classical dancing. The studios were vast and unheated, so cold that the children were allowed to keep on their woollen leggings and felt boots until their bodies began to generate heat. The saintly Maria, however, demonstrated movement in a thin tunic, providing yet another example of fortitude to her daughter. After class, Maria returned to the adjoining rehearsal studio to do her own *barre*.

As a teacher Maria was as influential as she was in forming the character of her only child. She demanded faultless technique combined with perfect musicality, and at the same time directed her pupils away from 'that dangerous path so tempting to the ballerina, of virtuoso effects for their own sake'. Star status was not the aim, but harmony of the whole.

At the end of the second year Maria choreographed a polka to Rachmaninov for Galina to dance at the spring concert which was in way of an examination, passport to the next grade class. This first public performance filled Galina with fear and dread, and anxiety completely overwhelmed any pleasure she might have enjoyed in executing a happy dance created by her mother. Nevertheless, she passed the test and moved up to the third form, still benefiting from Maria's tuition for another two years, until she was accepted into the intermediate class under Agrippina Vaganova, after whom the Leningrad Ballet School was renamed in 1957.

During the school years, the children performed in the tiny, well-equipped theatre which even had an orchestra pit although all it contained was a piano. It approximated as closely as possible to the real theatre and prepared the children for the stage as well as giving the teachers a chance to assess performing abilities. There are no Freudian overtones to Ulanova's early pleasure in dancing male roles, and she was proud to partner Tatiana (Tanya) Vecheslova, in, among other pieces, the clog dance from *La Fille mal gardée*. Vecheslova became Director of the Leningrad school and a ballet mistress of the Kirov company. They were an illustrious school duo.

Alongside the school performances—Ulanova recalls with particular fondness her part of the nymph in *The Satyr's Grotto* created to Grieg by Alexander Shirayev, one of her teachers—the pupils saw the professional productions and were inspired by Fokine's *Egyptian Nights* and *Chopiniana* (*Les Sylphides*). It was in this last work that she appeared in her graduation performance, albeit in the *corps*, and as the Sugar Plum Fairy in the *Nutcracker divertissement*. She made sufficient impression to join the company as a soloist, and once again danced in *Chopiniana*, this time professionally. Only four months later she was given the leading role of Odette-Odile in *Swan Lake*.

Maria Romanova was in the audience that night, 6 February 1929, to see her daughter's début in one of the most demanding roles ever created for a ballerina, requiring not only impeccable technique but the ability to perform the dual part of the lyrical swan-princess and the sharply glittering wizard's daughter. Ulanova was not physically strong and Maria was doubly anxious in *her* dual role of mother and teacher. When the moment came in Act III for Galina to execute the 32 *fouettés*, those rapid turns on *pointe* on one spot, Maria could bear it no longer. She left the box to pray in the theatre corridor and was spared the sight of her daughter travelling across the stage, ending not far from the wings where her father, Sergei, watched from his stage-manager's position. Silent man as he was, he made no comment then or at any performance. He treated her as he treated all the other dancers, with perfect professional support and no inkling of the affection he felt. Only once, many years later, when Ulanova was a Bolshoi dancer and came to Leningrad to dance Juliet at the Kirov, did he see her from the front of house and that night at home he voiced his approval. 'Not bad. You danced pretty well.' It was the highest praise.

The critics at her first *Swan Lake* were not wholly enthusiastic, and for many years she did not again undertake Odile and the *fouettés*. At that time Odette and Odile were often danced by two ballerinas and her Odette was well enough received. One critic wrote of her 'moving vulnerability'. Another spoke of 'a touching charm of diffidence and imperfect dancing', finding she had potential which she somehow refrained from using. Marina Semeyonova was the most popular ballerina in the company, with all the virtuosity that Ulanova seemed to lack, but Ulanova remained faithful to her own and her mother's precepts. In the current terminology, she continued to 'do her own thing' and her physical limitations—the short neck and arms—were brilliantly disguised by a slight characteristic head tilt and extended fingers. She had the frail vulnerability of those early screen heroines she had watched in her childhood and she retained this image throughout her dancing career, while her great theatrical artistry developed.

Above *Off-stage, Galina Ulanova appeared as a simple, unassuming young woman. On-stage, as Juliet in Leonid Lavrovsky's grandiose production of* Romeo and Juliet, *she became the exquisite, volatile, impassioned heroine of Shakespeare's romantic tragedy. In this picture she is partnered by Alexander Lapauri as Paris.*

Right *Galina Ulanova created the role of Tao Hoa in Lavrovsky's 1949 restaging of* The Red Poppy *originally produced in 1927 with music by Reinhold Glière. The story tells of a dancer, exploited by a vicious capitalist, who gives her life to save a crowd of revolutionary Chinese workers.*

During that first season she also danced Princess Florine in *The Sleeping Beauty* and a slave in *Le Corsaire*, a role she said 'eluded me completely'. In 1930 she made her debut as Aurora which was not a success and she never returned to the role. It was Giselle which she danced for the first time during the 1931–32 season which established her with the public and she continued to work on the role which has been described as the pinnacle of her art.

Since the Revolution, Albrecht had been portrayed as a feudal villain. With subtle changes which did not alter the social message, Ulanova and her partner, Konstantin Sergeyev, one of the initiators of the new Soviet Ballet, steered away from vulgar stereotyping and humanized the characters. Ulanova capitalized on her physical shortcomings and made Giselle a simple, apprehensive and distinctly unglamorous peasant girl. There was no artful flirtation, nothing coy. She fell in love with Albrecht and his irresponsibility and his betrayal were fatal for her. Even after death she remained faithful to him, and in Act II she urged him to resist the Wilis and save his life. She radiated pure love, and Albrecht watched her return to the tomb, her eyes fixed on him, and he repented.

In 1933 she once again essayed Odette, and this time critics and audiences were overwhelmed by her performance. As with Giselle, her interpretation embodied indestructible fidelity and love which touched the contemporary pulse. Such values could withstand the forebodings of ordinary citizens that the socialist state was not the best of all possible worlds. At the same time she complied to the needs of official Soviet art, and on both counts her prestige blossomed, and continued to blossom as she began to be cast in drama-ballets, emblematic of the period. Over the next two decades Rostislav Zakharov and then Leonid Lavrovsky, the two major choreographers of this genre, always cast Ulanova as the heroine of their works, both at the Kirov and the Bolshoi. Her powers of mime and her extraordinary expressiveness made her pre-eminent among the ballerinas of both companies, but it is fascinating to discover that when Eisenstein decided to cast her as Anastasia in his film, *Ivan the Terrible*, she failed her screen test. Her acting powers were confined to this type of ballet.

In 1934 Zakharov mounted *The Fountain of Bakhchisarei* in which Ulanova danced the Polish Princess Maria. The critics were in a catch-22 situation, some of them obliged to praise a politically approved ballet when they were not genuinely inspired. They managed to get round their inhibitions by describing Ulanova's performance as a sequence of sculptural poses rather than dance, albeit extolling her for her undeniably unmatched artistry. One described her *demi-arabesques* as being comparable to the mystery and charm of the Mona Lisa. Ulanova's own opinion of the highly charged plot of capture by the Tartar Khan Guirey and the murder of Maria by his jealous wife was unequivocal. Story and style combined to produce potent drama. 'If choreography based on ordinary simple steps is performed perfectly, it is sufficient to make a hardly perceptible movement, suggest a pose, raise your head or glance differently in order to alter a characterization or create a special atmosphere on stage.'

It was because she 'performed perfectly' that she drew from her audiences the deepest emotions, conveying to them the very essence of the joy of love or the pain of death as Giselle, Maria, Juliet. *Romeo and Juliet* was mounted for her at the Kirov in 1940 by Lavrovsky, a literal version with poses, turns and arabesques rather than fluid dance dominating the choreography. She performed it with the qualities she had brought to Giselle, vulnerability, innocence and an aura of romance culminating in sorrow and tragic death.

Other works, mostly based on mime, followed: *Cinderella*, *The Bronze Horseman*, *The Red Poppy* and *The Stone Flower*. They did not endure, and Anna Akhmatova, the poet, is reputed to have remarked that as a ballerina Ulanova was a non-starter, but as a mime artist she was a genius.

During the war years Ulanova was evacuated with the Kirov to Perm and Molotov, and in 1941 she won the Stalin Prize. In 1944 she joined the Bolshoi and received the Stalin Prize again in 1946, 1947 and 1950. In 1951, the year in which she danced *The Dying Swan* in Florence to outstanding acclaim, she was made a People's Artist of the RSFSR. In 1956 her Juliet and Giselle made her the toast of London and in 1957 she was awarded the Lenin Prize. In 1974 she was named a Hero of Socialist Work and received the Lenin Prize once more.

An honoured daughter of the Soviet Union, she appears never to have involved herself in politics, although there are still those who believe her success was partly due to state patronage and support. The only instance of public involvement was in 1955 when she signed a letter with other dancers accusing her former partner, Konstantin Sergeyev, then artistic director of the Kirov, of restricting the dancers' opportunities. This denunciation in the press did result in his resignation, and it is interesting to note that although he returned to the post later, he was dismissed in 1970 because of Makarova's defection to the West.

Ulanova's private life has been as discreet as her political views. She married twice, first to a stage director, Y. Zavadsky, and then to the designer Vadim Rindin who was made chairman of the Varna Competition in 1964. In 1962 she retired from dancing but, as her mother had done in Leningrad almost 40 years earlier, continued to teach and coach. When the Bolshoi visited London in 1986 Ulanova was with them, taking a back seat at press conferences and generally present in the audiences at the Royal Opera House with Yuri Grigorovich, the company's conservative director.

Vasiliev, an openly anti-Grigorovich man, was the first male dancer ever to be coached by Ulanova. The ballet was Grigorovich's cumbersome *Ivan the Terrible*, choreographed in the style in which Ulanova excelled, so it is understandable that she elected or had been asked to prepare Vasiliev for his role. Naturally they argued, he said afterwards, because they differed on the way certain sections should be done, but coach and performer had equal rights to a role and the end result was a combined effort. Their work together was productive because they had shared goals. 'Ulanova is always trying for the clearest possible expressiveness on the stage to achieve what in literature is described as being "the minimum of words, the maximum of sense".' 'Great emotion' Vasiliev elaborated, 'with great clarity.'

These final words could be taken as an epitaph to Galina Ulanova's remarkable dancing career.

E·R·I·K B·R·U·H·N

Of all the male dancers of his generation, Erik Bruhn was unmatched in his classical perfection and nobility of bearing. He was extremely handsome, he had a perfectly proportioned physique, his training was impeccable, his technique was immaculate and his performances in *Giselle*, *Swan Lake*, *La Sylphide* and *Les Sylphides*, in particular, stood as examples for his contemporaries, as well as aspiring students, to aim at. Even Nureyev considered him a role-model in the classical repertoire.

Bruhn was born in Copehagen, Denmark, on 3 October 1928. His father, who was an irrigation engineer, became ill and could not work. Instead he took to drink and gambling and when Erik was five his parents parted. His mother was a free-spirited, unconventional woman who ran a hairdressing salon. Erik had three sisters, two who were older and one younger, and when they started ballet classes Erik went too. Not only was it convenient to have all four children together but it was thought that the experience would also help to change his rather introspective and 'difficult' disposition.

His natural aptitude as a ballet student was quickly noticed by his teachers and at the age of nine his aunt, who lived with the family, took him to be auditioned at the Royal Danish Ballet School, which accepted him. He lived at home and although his academic work at school was below average and he remained emotionally withdrawn, his teachers at the ballet school recognized him as a very promising pupil—despite being at loggerheads with at least one ballet teacher.

In addition to a home life that was fairly fraught the Germans invaded Denmark on 9 April 1940, when life for all Danish citizens became full of tension and hazards. It was against this anxiety-ridden background that Bruhn completed his training. He made his début at the age of 16 in the Pantomime Theatre in the Tivoli Gardens in a Russian dance (in itself something of a dangerous act of defiance in that Nazi Germany and Soviet Russia had been locked in titanic struggle since 1941) choreographed by the great Harald Lander, dancer and subsequent Director of the Royal Danish Ballet. Just as Bruhn was about to start his solo British troops, who had liberated the city, arrived in the Tivoli Gardens and the audience deserted the theatre to welcome the soldiers.

Bruhn continued his studies for a further two years and was admitted into the Royal Danish Ballet, then under the direction of Harald Lander, in 1947. During the summer vacation, however, he was persuaded by another Danish dancer, Poul Gnatt, who had befriended Bruhn and who was on leave of absence from the Royal Danish Ballet, to accompany him to Britain where he was engaged to dance with an emergent British company, the Metropolitan Ballet.

E·R·I·K B·R·U·H·N

For the 18-year-old Bruhn, whose dance experience had been confined almost exclusively to the Bournonville repertoire of the Danish company, London was a revelation. He saw the (then) Sadler's Wells Ballet, with Margot Fonteyn, Moira Shearer and Beryl Grey as its current stars; he was astonished by the dancing of Jean Babilée with Roland Petit's Ballet de Champs d'Elysée; he loved the glamour attached to Colonel de Basil's original Ballet Russe, and was fascinated by Katherine Dunham and her Caribbean company and Carmen Amaya and her Spanish dancers. While taking daily class and touring with the Metropolitan Ballet, he fell in love with one of its dancers, the Rumanian-born ballerina Sonia Arova.

When the time came to return to Copenhagen and the comparatively enclosed world of the Royal Danish Ballet, he resolved to resign from the company—an astonishing and, some would think, foolhardy decision from a young dancer who had only just been admitted to one of the world's great classical companies and whose career had scarcely begun. To Bruhn's own astonishment Lander, when he received the young dancer's letter of resignation, proposed instead that he take six months leave of absence. Almost immediately he rejoined Metropolitan Ballet, whose impressive roster of dancers included Arova, Svetlana Beriosova (daughter of Nicholas Beriozoff who was ballet-master of the company), Colette Marchand, Celia Franca (who later founded the National Ballet of Canada), Poul Gnatt and Serge Perrault.

That subsequent six months with Metropolitan Ballet proved to be an invaluable experience for Bruhn. Not only did he dance in works from the Diaghilev repertoire—he was considered to be one of the finest exponents of the title role in Fokine's *Spectre of the Rose*—and in classical excerpts such as the Bluebird *pas de deux* from *The Sleeping Beauty* and the Black Swan *pas de deux* from *Swan Lake*, but John Taras created a fine new work, *Designs with Strings*, with Bruhn and Beriosova as leading dancers.

Throughout that period the relationship between Bruhn and Arova burgeoned, both professionally and personally. They danced together and found instinctive rapport, and their affection for one another grew constantly. When the six months were up and Bruhn was due to return to Denmark he presented Arova with a beautiful ruby and diamond engagement ring. At an emotional farewell the plan was that Arova would go to Copenhagen and meet Bruhn's family.

Back with the Royal Danish Ballet, Bruhn was chosen by Leonide Massine,

Erik Bruhn was considered the most stylistically perfect premier danseur *of his day, a quality exemplified in this photograph of him in* Don Quixote.

who was then guest choreographer with the company, to dance the leading role of the Hussar in his ballet *Le Beau Danube*, and to take another leading role in a revival of one of his most famous, controversial symphonic ballets, *Symphonie Fantastique*, to Berloz's symphony of that title. Bruhn scored a success in each work, particularly as the romantic Hussar who meets an old flame in the Prater in Vienna.

In June, 1949, Lander choreographed a string of excerpts from some of Bournonville's most famous ballets in which Bruhn performed two solos and a *pas de deux* with Margrethe Schanne from the second act of *La Sylphide*. Amongst the audience was Blevins Davis, President of the American Ballet Theatre Foundation; he was immensely impressed by Bruhn's dancing—and his exceptional beauty—and after the performance he went backstage and told Bruhn that he would be happy to recommend that Bruhn should dance with American Ballet Theatre. Bruhn was excited by the prospect but said that first he had to fulfil the season's contract with the Danish parent company but that he expected to be in Paris during the summer vacation with Sonia Arova. Davis replied that he, too, would be in Paris and suggested that Bruhn contact him at the Ritz Hotel.

Arova arrived in Copenhagen from Paris where her hopes of joining the Paris Opera Ballet had not been fulfilled—Serge Lifar, Director of the company, had made extravagant promises to engage both her and Bruhn, knowinng that the company policy was not to engage foreign dancers on a permanent basis. But her short stay in Copenhagen was a happy one: she got on well with Bruhn's Mother and her fiancé took her on an extended sight-seeing tour of the city and arranged for her to watch him taking the boys' class with the company.

When Arova returned to Paris, Bruhn once again asked Lander for leave of absence. To his surprise, Lander not only agreed but also told Bruhn that he was being promoted to Soloist (equal to Principal with other companies). During the summer Arova had arranged that she and Bruhn should dance with the Bordeaux Ballet but, after a preliminary visit had decided that the company was not of sufficiently high standard. As the arrangement had fallen through Bruhn found himself in Paris with a year's leave of absence and no company to dance with. Remembering Blevins Davis's invitation he called at the Ritz Hotel; Davis was not there but he had left a letter for Bruhn in which he said that Lucia Chase, having been apprised by Antony Tudor of Bruhn's excellence as a dancer (Tudor had been working as a guest choreographer with the Royal Swedish Ballet) was prepared to offer him a contract to dance with American Ballet Theatre.

Arova, of course, was 'terribly upset' at the thought of Bruhn leaving for America, but did nothing to hold him back. She did, secretly, write to Balanchine in the hope that she might be invited to join New York City Ballet or, at least, to study at the School of American Ballet, but she never received a reply.

Bruhn travelled to the United States on board the SS *America* in company with Blevins Davis. He was excited at the elegance of first class travel but somewhat disconcerted by Davis's sexual advances. He was even more disappointed on arrival in New York to discover that ABT would not be performing for six weeks, that everyone assumed that he was Davis's 'special friend' and that Davis expected him to stay with him on his estate in Independence, Missouri. He was eventually persuaded to go by Lucia Chase who was anxious that Davis, as 'Mr Moneybags', should be kept happy. Actually, Davis turned out to be 'very nice', to be an extravagant host who put his car at Bruhn's disposal, arranged for him to take class with a teacher in Kansas City and threw a big twenty-first birthday party for Bruhn at which Bess Truman, the President's wife, was present. In later years, after Blevins's death, Bruhn acknowledged his gratitude to the man for providing him with the first opportunity to dance in America.

One of the first ballets in which Bruhn appeared with ABT was John Taras's *Designs with Strings*, which he had first danced with the Metropolitan Ballet; he also danced in *The Nutcracker pas de deux* with Nana Gollner and Mary Ellen Moylan. Actually, during that first season with the company, he danced comparatively little (he was still a relatively unknown dancer and ABT possessed an impressive roster of males) but he 'laughed a lot, drank a lot and had lots and lots of fun'. He also became very friendly with Nora Kaye who had been rocketed to fame by her sensational success in Antony Tudor's first American ballet, *Pillar of Fire*.

When Bruhn returned to Copenhagen the Royal Danish Ballet was in turmoil: Harald Lander's direction of the company was being questioned by a certain faction and Bruhn, although he had no personal quarrel with Lander, was persuaded to write a critical statement which was published in the press which, of course, Lander found most upsetting. Lander and his wife subsequently left the Royal Danish Ballet which was then directed by Niels Bjorn Larsen, one of the company's senior dancers. Factional elements continued to play in-house politics, however, and prompted Bruhn to write to Lucia Chase asking to rejoin ABT. In due course she answered his letter, inviting him to join the company for the 1951–52 season.

This time he was given more roles to dance, including two more or less plotless ballets, the world première of Bronislava Nijinska's *Schumann Concerto*, to the

Schumann Piano Concerto in A minor, and William Dollar's *Constantia*, an abstract *ballet blanc* to Chopin's Piano Concerto in F minor, which alluded to Chopin's dedication of the work to Constantia Gladowska. He also danced the *Don Quixote pas de deux* and in the white *pas de deux* of Frederick Ashton's *Les Patineurs*. Although he sometimes deputized for the company's *premier danseur*, Igor Youskevitch, when he was indisposed and there would be groans from the audience when the announcement was made, Bruhn's immaculate dancing began to be noticed by the critics and the *cognoscenti*, and by the end of the season the groans sometimes gave way to cheers.

Bruhn's one regret at this time was that he had undertaken to return to the Royal Danish Ballet for a period of two years. On returning to Copenhagen his role in the Lander affair was obviously not forgotten and he was the subject of some vicious attacks in the press. Even so his performances, especially in the classics—*Swan Lake, The Sleeping Beauty, The Nutcracker*—began to mature to a marked degree, not just in his marvellously noble and aristocratic portrayal of princely roles, but also in the depth of his characterization of what were usually cardboard cavaliers. In particular he gave great thought to the role of James in Bournonville's great Romantic classic *La Sylphide*. He had been taught the mime for this role when he was a student but had been unable to find any satisfaction in merely copying the traditional gestures. When he came to dance it he prepared the part with great care, finding what he considered were the motivational reasons for James's infatuation with the Sylphide, attempting to discover the psychological truth in the part. This twentieth-century approach to a nineteenth-century role revitalized it, but it was not until the company gave a brilliant season at the Royal Opera House, Covent Garden, in 1953 and Bruhn received rave reviews, not only for his superb dancing but also for his interpretation of James, that the management of the Royal Danish Ballet began to realize what a magnificent dancer they had in their company.

Before he left the Royal Danish Ballet, Harald Lander had brought over the great Russian teacher Vera Volkova to the school. Volkova had studied with Agrippina Vaganova upon whose system of teaching the Kirov and Bolshoi ballets are based, and from 1936 to 1950 had had her own school in London, an influential teacher to a whole generation of British ballet dancers. Bruhn spent many hours talking and working with her and she was instrumental in his perfecting his classical technique, adding Russian strength and vitality to the Danish speed and precision. Bruhn's relationship with Volkova became artistically intense—she filled him with more information than he was able to absorb and he became nervous about his performances. When he returned to ABT, however, in 1954, he found that she had given him a 'freedom and richness that were unique', and her teaching was instrumental in his rapid climb to the top with his adopted American company.

Bruhn and Arova, although still nominally engaged, had not seen each other for five years. Arova, having no parent company, had lived a nomadic life, guesting with various companies around the world, from the Festival Ballet in London to the Komaki Ballet in Japan. In 1954 she was with the Marquis de Cuevas company in Paris; at one of the Marquis's soirées in his sumptuous apartment on the Quai d'Orsay whom should she meet but Blevins Davis . . . Arova was full of questions about Bruhn and the result of their meeting was that Davis promised to make enquiries about the possibility of her joining ABT. Two weeks later she received a cable saying that she had been accepted by the company and to take the next boat to New York.

Arova was both overjoyed and apprehensive at the prospect of seeing Bruhn again. She was rapidly aware that he was a different person to the one she had known: 'He was close to dancers like Scott Douglas and Ray Barra . . . My feelings were that we should end our relationship.' They had a long talk in which both dancers decided that they should conclude their engagement, while remaining close friends and promising to 'keep our beautiful memories alive'. Arova stayed with ABT for three years and although she and Bruhn did not often dance together they did appear in two important works, Massine's *Mam'zelle Angot* and once more in Taras's *Designs with Strings*—the ballet which brought their relationship full circle.

During this period with ABT Bruhn reached a milestone of his career when he danced in *Giselle* with Alicia Markova. It was a matinée performance on 1 May 1955, at the old Metropolitan Opera House. He had rehearsed intensely with Markova (Anton Dolin had put in a brief appearance at rehearsals, during which he had done nothing but insult her; she had him barred from further visits) and she was immensely helpful, both in solving certain technical problems and also in preparing his interpretation of Albrecht. His performance brought ecstatic cheers from the audience and enthusiastic reviews that referred to 'the most notable event of the season,' and 'one of those electrifying performances when everyone is aware that something extraordinary is happening.' It was indeed extraordinary: Bruhn was suddenly the talk of the ballet world, a new international star, heralded as one of the greatest male dancers in the West. It was not just a tremendous personal triumph for Bruhn but a providential piece of timing for Lucia Chase who had been told, the previous morning, that her two stars, Alicia Alonso and Igor Youskevitch, were leaving ABT to join the rival company

Ballet Russe de Monte Carlo. There was, said Bruhn, a marked changed in Chase's attitude towards him: she had previously turned down his request for promotion; now she told him 'I am going to make you one of my stars!'

In 1955 Bruhn was invited back to Copenhagen to repeat his success in *Giselle* with Markova, which he did. They also danced the ballet on Danish TV. While in Copenhagen he also danced the role of Romeo in Frederick Ashton's version of *Romeo and Juliet* which he had mounted that same year. Bruhn was acclaimed for his performance, which he repeated with equal success at the Edinburgh Festival that autumn, although the ballet itself did not prove popular and was dropped from the Danish repertoire. (Bruhn's compatriot, Peter Schaufuss, a great virtuoso dancer, revived the work for London Festival Ballet 30 years later.) Bruhn enjoyed that season with the Royal Danish Ballet—and enjoyed the reunion with his mother, aunt and sisters.

Bruhn retured to New York and ABT as one of its stars, although his exclusive contract with the company precluded him from dancing with the Danish company when it made its first visit to America in 1956. His feelings about stardom were, however, ambiguous. He felt that Lucia Chase was overworking him, and there was 'a lot of tension' between them; for long periods Bruhn refused to speak to his Director. If he was overworked he nevertheless delivered some wonderful performances, frequently partnering Nora Kaye and garnering rave reviews. He danced in Robert Joffrey's Romantic pastiche, *Pas des Déesses*; Anton Dolin's bravura piece for four male virtuosos, *Variations for Four*; Kenneth MacMillan's *Journey*—a ballet created to exploit the dramatic talents of Nora Kaye; Herbert Ross's *Concerto* and *Tristan*; Alfred Rodrigues's *Blood Wedding*, and partnered Kaye in the second act of *Swan Lake* and in *Giselle*. He also created a plotless ballet, *Festa*, to music by Rossini which was a popular success, although he did not dance in it himself. That same season Sonia Arova decided to leave the company. She had established a relationship with one of the company's dancers, Job Sanders, whom she married and they worked together in Europe. The marriage was not a success and they were divorced in 1959. Bruhn later confessed to having regrets that he had not married Arova some years before when they were first engaged, but 'I was nineteen, she was twenty. I wanted to marry her but she told me I was too young.' In later years his initial ardour had cooled.

One of the benefits of stardom was the opportunity to pick and choose roles. Bruhn had seen a ballet by the Swedish choreographer Birgit Cullberg, *Miss Julie*, based on the play by August Strindberg. He was fascinated by the role of Jean, a valet, who seduces the aristocratic daughter of the house. It was a

Left *Erik Bruhn partnering Nadia Merina in the* pas de deux *from Marius Petipa's ballet* Don Quixote, *with music by Alois Minkus.*

Right *Erik Bruhn with Kirsten Simone in the Royal Danish Ballet production of* Miss Julie, *a work by Birgit Cullberg based on the play by August Strindberg.*

highly dramatic role and in considerable contrast to the noble princes and romantic heroes he usually played. He prevailed upon Lucia Chase to acquire the ballet for him, which she did. He also thought that the title role would be a marvellously dramatic one for Nora Kaye. Curiously, Cullberg herself told Chase that she thought Bruhn quite wrong for the role of Jean—though nothing was said to him. During rehearsals Kaye announced that she disliked the part; the role was given to Violette Verdy and both she and Bruhn achieved a sensational success in the ballet. Bruhn was especially pleased to have shown he could play a villain with conviction and had broken the mould of the golden-boy image.

At the conclusion of the 1957–58 season ABT was in the midst of a financial crisis and the company was disbanded, perforce, until the spring of 1960. Bruhn was invited to return to the Royal Danish Ballet, now under the direction of Frank Schaufuss (father of Peter Schaufuss). When Bruhn arrived in Copenhagen he found the company in the midst of another turmoil. There was a strong movement to bring back Lander but 50 per cent of the dancers were against it. The upheaval became so great that Bruhn took refuge in Germany from all the litigation and rows and left his lawyer to negotiate on his behalf. The final result was that Niels Bjorn Larsen was reinstated as ballet-master and Bruhn's contract stated that he would dance for three months of the three succeeding years.

Almost the first thing he did was to restage *Giselle*, although he did not dance in it himself. The production was very successful and received unqualified praise. Bruhn chose Kirsten Simone as his partner in the company and together they danced in *La Sylphide, Miss Julie*, and Roland Petit's *Carmen*.

Bruhn was now 31, at the height of his powers and the top of his profession. In the autumn of 1959 he received an invitation to dance with New York City Ballet. He was delighted at the chance to work with George Balanchine; he had already danced in a number of Balanchine works with the Royal Danish Ballet and ABT, but he felt that working with Balanchine himself would be a challenge to widen his interpretive art. He was also pleased to know that Maria Tallchief (who had been married to Balanchine) would also be rejoining the company; Bruhn had a tremendous admiration for this strong, dramatic dancer of American Indian extraction.

Bruhn's début with New York City Ballet was in Balanchine's one-act version of *Swan Lake* and with Tallchief as his partner he achieved a sensational success. He also partnered her in *The Nutcracker* and danced with Patricia Wilde in Balanchine's *Night Shadow* and *Divertimento No 15*. All these performances were hailed in the press with glowing enthusiasm. Yet something was wrong. He was called into the office of Betty Cage, administrative director of the company, and told that Balanchine had the feeling that he was being 'auditioned' by Bruhn. A meeting was called and Bruhn was astonished to be told by Balanchine that 'You are a star, what do you want in this company?' Bruhn pointed out that he had been invited to join, that he had asked for no special treatment or star billing. Balanchine retracted his statements, saying that he had 'misunderstood', but the damage was done. Bruhn continued to feel out of place in the company, that Balanchine resented his box-office appeal which went against all his precepts about the ballets being more important than the dancers. (Though that was not to prevent him engaging a megastar, Baryshnikov, some years later.)

Bruhn returned to Copenhagen where, at his mother's suggestion, he bought the family house from her instead of building something new for himself. In 1960 he rejoined the newly reconstructed ABT, dancing with Tallchief (who had also left New York City Ballet) and Claude Bessy. In 1960 ABT visited Russia where the performances of Bruhn and Tallchief in the Black Swan *pas de deux* 'roused the Russian public into a frenzy'. During this time the emotionally outgoing and extrovert Tallchief had announced to Bruhn that she was in love with him, was going to divorce her husband and marry him. Bruhn was dismayed and resolved to break up their partnership when the opportunity occurred. That opportunity came when they were back in the United States when both dancers had a particularly violent quarrel and Bruhn said enough was enough. Tallchief left in a rage, saying that she had heard that there was a Russian in Paris who had defected and she would make *him* her partner.

The Russian, of course, was Rudolf Nureyev. And the extraordinary thing is that while Nureyev was dancing in Deauville with the de Cuevas company— his first engagement in the West—Tallchief saw him and became friendly. He told her of his admiration for Bruhn (he had seen an amateur film of Bruhn's dancing, made during ABT's visit to Moscow) and Tallchief was instrumental in introducing the two men. She took Nureyev to Copenhagen from Frankfurt, where he had been filming for German TV, and telephoned Bruhn at home from the bar of the Hotel Angeleterre, suggesting they all have a drink together. It was a strained, uneasy meeting, and Bruhn made an excuse to leave after an hour.

Nureyev stayed on in Copenhagen, taking lessons with Volkova, class with the Royal Danish Ballet and watching performances in the evening. Gradually, Bruhn and Nureyev established a wary friendship—although, with Tallchief often present, it was an emotionally charged atmosphere which resulted in some temperamental scenes.

Nureyev was invited by Fonteyn to take part in a gala in London. When he returned to Copenhagen he stayed some three months in Bruhn's family home; Bruhn's mother did not take to the Russian visitor but the friendship between the dancers grew stronger despite some tempestuous rows and scenes—Bruhn the cool, reserved Dane, Nureyev the passionate, volatile Russian. Bruhn once accused Nureyev of coming out of Russia in order to destroy him. Nureyev was deeply upset at this but realized that their frequent upsets were inflamed by a world press which continually compared them as artists. Bruhn himself referred to them as 'two comets colliding and exploding'.

In 1962 both dancers were guest artists with the Royal Ballet at Covent Garden, Bruhn staging and dancing in Bournonville's *Flower Festival at Genzano*, and both of them appearing in *Giselle, Swan Lake, The Sleeping Beauty* and *Les Sylphides*. Both men drew ecstatic reviews, and their differing styles were once more compared and applauded by factional fans. Bruhn was partnering Nadia Nerina and Nureyev was paired with Fonteyn—the beginning of their world-famous partnership. Bruhn and Nureyev shared an apartment and spent a lot of time together. Sometimes they would have a lot of fun, sometimes it would be the explosive rows. All of Bruhn's friends have said that he was essentially a very private person, an instinctive loner if never lonely. Certainly he never allowed himself to be 'possessed' by anyone and if a friendship became too intense, as with Maria Tallchief, he would unhesitatingly cool it or even conclude it altogether.

One of the splendid partnerships that Bruhn developed during the sixties, which also became a firm and lasting friendship, was with the Italian ballerina Carla Fracci. Their association was initiated by another friend, Christopher Allan, one-time press officer for ABT, subsequently working with a large theatrical agency. He saw Fracci dancing at the Scala, Milan, and was entranced by her grace, technique and charm. Back in New York he suggested to Bruhn that he might introduce her to American audiences. Bruhn, who had seen Fracci dance in London, was enthusiastic, and so Allan arranged for them to dance together for the NBC TV network in excerpts from *La Sylphide*. The two dancers established an instant rapport that was to develop into a distinguished partnership.

In 1962 Bruhn made a guest appearance with Arova on tour with the Australian Ballet, dancing in Peggy van Praagh's production of *Swan Lake, Les Sylphides* and *Coppelia* in which Bruhn made his debut as Franz. Wanting to see as many Bruhn performances as possible, Nureyev joined Bruhn and Arova in Sydney where the three were constant companions.

Back in New York Bruhn was offered another contract with ABT, but as Lucia Chase suggested the same terms as three years before Bruhn turned it down.

Instead, he went to Milan and danced with Fracci in *Giselle*. Both artists recognized they had established a magical partnership, something that was very special to them both. From Milan Bruhn returned to Copenhagen where he spent some time teaching and also received a major honour, being made a Knight of the Order of Danebrog. That same year he also received the Nijinsky Prize in Paris.

The previous year Bruhn's mother had died, suddenly, while Bruhn and Nureyev were staying at the house. The immediate cause was a blood clot but a post-mortem also revealed cancer. It was a terrible shock but even so Bruhn performed in *Carmen* the following night. Nureyev's presence gave him great emotional support which Bruhn said helped to 'bind their friendship'. Now, alone in the house a year later, he undertook considerable renovation.

In 1963 Bruhn received another invitation to dance with New York City Ballet. Despite the unhappy experience with the company in 1959, and against his own feelings of doubt, he signed a contract to appear during 1963-64. Once again he repeated his successes in *Swan Lake* with Tallchief—who had also rejoined—and *The Nutcracker, Divertimento No 15* and *Night Shadow*, but there was a row over his appearance in *Apollo*. Balanchine had taken Bruhn through the role himself but there had been no rehearsal with the other artists involved; for some reason this was refused so Bruhn, in turn, refused to go on. He never danced the role although Balanchine himself had said 'You are *the* Apollo!'

During the season Bruhn developed mysterious stomach pains. He was tested for cancer, with negative results. He thought that it might be emotional stress, brought on by his unhappiness with the company, so he resigned after only a few weeks of the season. The pains, however, continued, intermittantly, for the next 12 years.

Throughout the rest of the sixties Bruhn continued to guest with many companies around the world—with the Paris Opera Ballet in *Giselle*, partnering the great French ballerina Yvette Chauvire; with the Harkness Ballet, in which he performed in Stuart Hodes' *The Abyss*, a dramatic work involving the rape of a girl; he also created a new work for the company, *Scottish Fantasy*, with music by George Crum. He danced again with the Royal Danish Ballet, in *Miss Julie, Carmen* and *La Sylphide*. He starred with the Royal Swedish Ballet in *Giselle* and returned again to the Paris Opera Ballet to perform in George Skibine's version of *Daphnis and Chloe* and the *Don Quixote pas de deux*, partnering Claude Bessy who had been responsible for inviting him to the company.

Although his dancing continued to receive the greatest praise and vociferous acclaim wherever he went it is notable that not one of the major choreographers whose works he performed—Ashton, Balanchine, Roland Petit, Lichine et al.—created anything new for him. In particular he was sorry not to have performed in more Ashton works and he cherished a hope that, one day, Ashton would create a special role for him. It never happened.

In 1967 Lucia Chase succeeded in luring Bruhn back to ABT, on the understanding that she would also engage Carla Fracci, which she did. That season they gave memorable performances of *Giselle* and *La Sylphide*, establishing a partnership that many critics thought rivalled that of Fonteyn and Nureyev—although, of course, the repertoire of those dancers was far wider. It is strange that Bruhn never danced with Fonteyn, although he came close to doing so when it was proposed that Bruhn and Fracci, Fonteyn and Nureyev and six other dancers should undertake a tour. The idea did not materialize. According to Bruhn, Fonteyn was unenthusiastic about including Fracci: 'There was room for only one ballerina on that tour.'

During the middle 1960s Bruhn also undertook to stage several versions of the classics. His first major production was *La Sylphide* for the National Ballet of Canada in December, 1964—a production which he repeated for the Rome Opera Ballet in 1966 and the Royal Swedish Ballet in 1968. It was, of course, a great success—his long association with the Bournonville classic made sure of that. He followed that with an equally successful, though somewhat controversial, *Swan Lake* for the same company in March, 1967. The most controversial aspect of the production was the substitution of an evil Black Queen for the usual figure of von Rothbart, the sorcerer who holds the swan queen, Odette, in thrall. But although the critics questioned the change the ballet has remained one of the most popular works in the repertoire to this day.

While contracted to dance with companies all over the world, Bruhn was persuaded by the intendant of the Royal Swedish Opera House, Goeren Gentile, to become the Director of the Royal Swedish Ballet. The offer was made in 1964 but not taken up until 1967. It proved a difficult task: the standard of performance was poor and Bruhn found a considerable amount of opposition, both within the company and in the Swedish press which was particularly vicious in its criticisms of his policies. Nevertheless he did an enormous amount of productive work with the company, and not the least important part of his administration was his establishment of a ballet school, which lasted until 1971. During that time Gentile and his family became close and valued friends and Bruhn—like so many of Gentile's colleagues—was shattered by the tragic death of Gentile and his two daughters in a car accident in Sardinia, just prior to his taking up the appointment of Director of the Metropolitan Opera in New York.

In 1970 Natalia Makarova had defected from the Kirov Ballet in London and her first engagements were with ABT in America. Bruhn was scheduled to partner her in *Giselle* but at the last minute had to cancel his performance because of yet another attack of the excruciating stomach pains which he had suffered since 1963. He did, subsequently, dance with her in the ballet (which precipitated a jealous reaction from Carla Fracci) as well as partnering her to great acclaim in his own production of *La Sylphide* in the spring of 1971.

That same year, after performing with ABT at the Kennedy Center in Washington, Bruhn announced his retirement from dancing—precipitated by the terrible stomach pains which had bedevilled his performances in *Coppelia* and *La Sylphide*. It was an announcement received with deep regret by many of Bruhn's friends and colleagues, not least Lucia Chase, who was facing the loss of one of her great stars.

In 1973, while at home in Copenhagen and rehearsing an appearance in the play *Rashomon*, he collapsed with agonizing intestinal pains and was rushed to hospital. Five doctors variously diagnosed appendicitis, infection of the liver, kidneys and gall bladder. Finally they operated for appendicitis. After several hours they discovered he was suffering, and had been suffering for 12 years, from a perforated ulcer, undetected by numerous X-rays.

Following recuperation Bruhn returned once again to perform in ballet this time in the character role of Madge, the evil witch in *La Sylphide*, with the National Ballet of Canada during the New York Season in 1974. In December of that year he finally made an acclaimed appearance in *Rashomon* in Copenhagen. In January, 1975, he appeared at the ABT Thirty-fifth Anniversary Gala in an excerpt from *Miss Julie*. In the late seventies he also performed as Dr Coppelius in *Coppelia*, as The Man in MacMillan's *Las Hermanas*, in John Neumeier's turgid exposition of *Hamlet*, entitled *Hamlet Connotations*, and in the title role in James Clouser's full-length work *Rasputin—The Holy Devil*, created for his own Space/Dance/Theater in conjunction with Fort Worth Ballet, Texas. With typical style and panache Bruhn had successfully bridged the gap between *premier danseur noble* and character dancer.

Constantly called upon to lecture, teach and perform, Bruhn was very selective about what he undertook in the late seventies. In 1983 he was invited to become Director of the National Ballet of Canada, a position he accepted with great pleasure and dedication. He inspired the talented young dancers of that company with a great sense of loyalty and commitment, and had great plans for the future. Then, sadly and suddenly, at dinner one night with Glen Tetley and friends, he complained of chest pains. After tests the following day the doctors diagnosed cancer; within three weeks, on 1 April 1986, he was dead. 'It was,' Tetley said, 'As if, knowing the prognosis, he lost all the will to live.'

Erik Bruhn's achievements will be perpetuated by the Erik Bruhn Prize, an annual award given to competing dancers associated with the four companies with which Bruhn gave some of his greatest performances, The Royal Danish Ballet, the National Ballet of Canada, American Ballet Theatre and the Royal Ballet. For those who were lucky enough to see him dance, and to know him personally, he will be remembered as a great artist and a human being who was always his own man.

'I cannot remember ever not being on the stage. I felt at home there, and was never nervous until the day I stopped dancing.' Nora Kaye performed with the Metropolitan Opera Ballet at the age of eight for a fee of 50 cents and grew up to be one of the great dramatic dancers of the twentieth century. Kenneth MacMillan, inspired by her extraordinary talent to create two works for her, *Winter's Eve* and *Journey*, described her as 'the first great American ballerina'. She was probably the first to reverse the tradition of taking a Russian name for professional reasons. Born of Russian parents she dropped the genuine Koreff for the simple American Kaye.

Her parents were among the hundreds of thousands of immigrants from Europe. Being Jewish it is likely that the decision was forced on them by the long series of pogroms and persecutions carried out by the authorities, but whatever the reason they never relinquished their sense of Russian identity. Her father may well have been an actor, for Nora Kaye recorded that he had worked with Stanislavsky. There was certainly an awareness of theatrical potential because Mrs Koreff (creative in her own way, designing and making hats for New York ladies) decided early that her daughter could be a dancer.

Nora was born on 1 January 1920. In 1925 she was enrolled in a class given by Alexis Kosloff, a graduate of the Russian Imperial Ballet School in Moscow. A year later mild diabetes, blamed on her vegetarian diet, put an end to physical activities for the time being. When she was well enough to resume, it was in Margaret Curtis's children's classes at the Metropolitan Opera Ballet school, and under this auspice she appeared in *William Tell* and other operas in dances choreographed by the ballet-mistress of the Metropolitan Opera, Rosina Galli.

Mrs Koreff now decided that Nora should be taught by the renowned Mikhail Fokine who had been ballet-master of the Maryinsky Theatre before she had left Russia. She took Nora for an audition to his house on the corner of 72nd Street and Riverside Drive, when he agreed to take her without payment on the condition that she studied with him alone to become an exclusive product of his style.

Young as she was, the child realized that she was not being taught technique. Fokine began his classes in a small upstairs room with haphazard warm-up exercises, often delegating the task to another teacher. When the pupils descended to the larger studio for centre work, he taught dances from his ballets, demonstrating his own style and theories, stressing the importance of beauty, line and movement. Arms were held loose, with limpid wrists and soft elbows, hips were not held rigid, but one thrust out to give a curved line. All that he disliked in Petipa's technique he eliminated, and although he was a brilliant

coach of his own work, young Nora Koreff missed the physical discipline instilled by her earlier teachers, and the correction necessary for improvement. Consequently, without Fokine's knowledge, she again attended classes at the Metropolitan Opera Ballet School on Monday, Wednesday and Friday and learned the classical technique which, on Tuesday, Thursday and Saturday she was not allowed to use except in Fokine's development of it. As for traditional schooling, there were a series of tutors hired by her mother to fill in the gaps at home.

Nora Kaye's first official contract was signed when she was 14 and was engaged to dance for a season with the Metropolitan Opera Ballet. She earned 12 dollars a week, and the document is reputedly still in the theatre archives. A year later she joined the Lincoln Kirstein-George Balanchine American Ballet company which became the resident ballet at the Metropolitan Opera House, taking over from the existing Opera Ballet group. Describing the dancers' function as being 'a sort of moving scenery to give the audience something to look at while the singers rested their voices', she became progressively disenchanted and made the decision to go into the commercial theatre. There was no major American ballet company which could offer continuing employment, and so Nora Kaye appeared on Broadway in *Great Lady* which featured a classical ballet. Among the dancers were Alicia Alonso, André Eglevsky and Jerome Robbins who were all later to join the American Ballet Theatre. The show ran for three weeks, but the dancers were employed together by the same producer for *Stars in Your Eyes* with Ethel Merman and Jimmy Durante and the famous Russian ballerina Tamara Toumanova. Happy with the direction her career had taken, Kaye did not join other dancers auditioning for the Ballet Russe de Monte Carlo, or show any interest in the auditions for American Ballet Theatre in 1939 when Richard Pleasant and Lucia Chase first formed their company. It was only due to the persuasion of friends that Nora Kaye finally agreed to attend, an act which changed her life. Fokine was conducting the audition and hired her for the *corps de ballet* to begin rehearsals on 1 October for the inaugural season which was to open on 11 January 1940 at the Center Theater, Radio City.

The first weeks of rehearsals were reminiscent of her childhood classes as Fokine worked with the dancers on *Les Sylphides* and *Carnival*. The arrival of Antony Tudor from England changed every perception as she began working on his revival of *Jardin aux Lilas*, calling him 'the choreographer who gave life

Nora Kaye in one of her most famous roles, Lizzie Borden, in Agnes de Miele's powerful dance-drama Fall River Legend. *Although highly proficient in the classics, it was as a dramatic dancer that Kaye was unrivalled in American ballet.*

to all my as yet unformed aspirations'. She thought the ballet the most beautiful she had ever seen. Her own part in the *corps* was small, the girl who spies on the unfaithful heroine, Caroline, as she meets her past love, but it was Tudor's method which inspired her—literally 'method', for he applied Stanislavsky's approach to dance; 'the method' she had heard about from her father and from actors was applied by Tudor as he sought from his dancers every detail of the characters they were playing. Fokine, whom she adored, was concerned only with the fluidity of the body, but Tudor believed that the movements should be motivated by the mind. Two years later, when he created *Pillar of Fire* with Kaye as Hagar, who finds love when she thinks she had destroyed her chances, the psychological insight was revelatory. He probed her thoughts and only when he had settled where Hagar lived, what she wore, what she liked to eat, her past experiences, did he begin to work on the way she would move.

The première on 8 April 1942 caused a sensation. To music by Arnold Schoenberg (*Verklarte Nacht*) and with scenery and costumes by Jo Mielziner, the audience at the Metropolitan Opera were overwhelmed by the unbearable tension concealing Hagar's yearning, applauding Kaye as a ballerina of unrivalled dramatic power and *Pillar of Fire* as a masterwork. At the age of 22 there was no doubt that Nora Kaye was a star. Likewise, Hugh Laing, the English dancer who also joined the company in 1939 and partnered her in the ballet, was catapulted into public adulation. Looking back, Kaye was to say to friends that she owed everything to Tudor and Laing, they took her to the right restaurants, taught her what to eat and wear and read—their own Pygmalion.

Tudor's next work for Kaye and Laing was *Dim Lustre*, danced to Richard Strauss's *Burleske in D* and with costumes designed by the three Englishwomen who together went under the name of Motley. The theme was recollections of past love by Kaye as The Lady with Him, and Laing as The Gentleman with Her. Also in the cast were Muriel Bentley (with whom a very young Kaye had performed a dancing double act covered in blue paint at Radio City), Rosella Hightower, and Tudor himself in a variation called 'He Wore a White Tie'.

By 1946 Kaye was dancing the main ballerina roles in the classics and in works created and revived for the company, including Balanchine's *Apollo* and Tudor's *Romeo and Juliet*. She was also married to the violinist Isaac Stern. In June that year, with the other dancers of American Ballet Theatre she sailed for England on the *Queen Mary*, not yet reverted from carrying troops during the war in which the cabins accomodated nine passengers instead of four. Partially prepared for austerity Britain, Nora Kaye and Muriel Bentley asked the waiter at the Savoy (where they were staying for $6 a night) what they might have

Right Antony Tudor created several major roles for Nora Kaye. Here she is pictured with Hugh Laing, a frequent partner, in Dim Lustre, an evanescent work in which a simple gesture, a whiff of perfume, release nostalgic memories of previous romances.

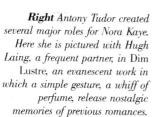

Left Nora Kaye as Odette in American Ballet Theatre's production of Swan Lake. Her strong stage presence and virtuoso technique made her an outstanding executant of the double role in this most popular of classical ballets.

for breakfast. Anything they wished, he replied. They decided on eggs boiled for three minutes. As the waiter was about to leave the room he said, 'May I have the eggs please?' It was a hard lesson for Americans whose deprivations had been minimal, but they were to discover that there were no hamburgers either, and very little fresh fruit. Clothes too, proved a problem. Walking along the Strand in nylons and high heels, fur jackets and silk dresses, they were whistled at and propositioned. With clothes coupons limiting Englishwomen to the equivalent of one new coat a year, such affluence implied only one profession.

The opening night at the Royal Opera House, Covent Garden (where the company was billed as The Ballet Theatre, New York, on the insistence of the General Administrator, David Webster) provided a welcome that has always been repeated by London audiences whenever the company has returned. *Les Sylphides* in which Nora Kaye danced with Alicia Alonso, Barbara Fallis and André Eglevsky, was considered more athletic than romantic, but Jerome Robbins's *Fancy Free* was rapturously received ('Grace, gusto and virility' said *The Observer*) and the Black Swan *pas de deux*, in which Kaye was partnered by Eglevsky, inspired the critic of *The Times* to write: 'Miss Kaye accomplished the 32 *fouettés* with a final touch of exhultant brilliance that excelled anything seen here in years, including performances before the war by the various Monte Carlo companies.'

Back in New York, in 1948, Agnes de Mille created for Nora Kaye a role for which she will always be remembered, that of Lizzie Borden in *Fall River Legend*. It opened in fact to a less than half-full house, with Kaye unwell and unable to dance, and Alicia Alonso taking over. (There was a current battle over billing between the two dancers which concluded when Alonso formed her own company in Cuba.) It was Kaye's imprint, however, that has remained on the work, the transition from agonized vulnerability to murderous passion demonstrating her emotional power. De Mille, one of American Ballet Theatre's original group of choreographers, wrote of Kaye that she had 'an ability to suggest more with sparser means than anyone in our time . . . she wore suffering like a flower, and when her arms lifted on a breath, her dark head turned, and her eyes opened, it was with the wonder of a stricken animal'.

Tudor started the new decade with an uncharacteristic, somewhat sentimental work, *Nimbus*, in which a working girl dreams of herself as an ethereal creature whose grace and beauty charms the man of her dreams. Kaye and Laing, with Diana Adams as The Dream, danced to music by Louis Gruenberg. It was Tudor's last work for American Ballet Theatre for six years, but not his last for Nora Kaye, who followed him and Jerome Robbins to New York City Ballet where both created new works for her. Robbins's *The Cage*, with music by Stravinsky and costumes by Ruth Sobotka, was a horrific ballet based on insects cannibalizing their lovers; Tudor's *La Gloire*, in 1952, returned to psychological ground, with Kaye as a great actress fearful of her understudy's burgeoning talents. It was not a work of any significance and it is obvious that Tudor's choreographic philosophy did not fit easily into the NYCB repertoire. Kaye, too, was out of place, unsuited to Balanchine's plotless ballets. Tudor's 'method' had no function in works in which the ballerina was required only to execute the brilliant choreography with perfect technique and no emotion.

Before returning to American Ballet Theatre which, with its wide range of ballets, suited her so well, Nora Kaye danced in Japan, with one permanently memorable night when she was performing the Black Swan *pas de deux*. During the 32 *fouettés* she became aware of a slight disturbance among the audience, rustling and movement throughout the auditorium. Determined not to be distracted she continued to dance, and only when she had completed the variation and gone into the wings did someone slip a coat over her shoulders and lead her swiftly out of doors into the street. As they stepped outside, the theatre burst into flames. One trusts the audience made as swift an exit. The incident says much for Japanese discipline—and Nora Kaye's.

In August 1956, American Ballet Theatre gave its third season at Covent Garden, and Lucia Chase organized a dinner at the Savoy to introduce Kenneth MacMillan to Nora Kaye. He had first seen her dance on the company's initial visit to London a decade earlier, and had been a great admirer ever since. She was very much a MacMillan dancer, with her exceptionally compelling stage presence and dramatic ability. The outcome of the meeting was an invitation for MacMillan to create a ballet for her which would be rehearsed in Monte Carlo during the American Ballet Theatre's Christmas season there, and premièred at the San Carlos Opera House in Lisbon in January. MacMillan decided on Benjamin Britten's *Variations on a Theme by Frank Bridge* as the score for the Carson McCullers-based story of a blind girl in love with a young man unaware of her affliction. Nicholas Geordiadis designed the sets and costumes for the work which was finally given the title of *Winter's Eve*. John Kriza and Nora Kaye scored personal triumphs as the tragic lovers, and the Lisbon critics were complimentary about the work. In New York there was praise for the artists but less enthusiasm for the ballet. The American critics were much more receptive to the workshop performance of MacMillan's second work for Kaye, *Journey*, the following May, in which a woman is accompanied by three messengers as she travels towards death. Three of the company's leading male dancers, Erik

Above *Nora Kaye in Jerome Robbins's ballet* The Cage. *Set to Stravinsky's Concerto in D, the highly dramatic libretto tells of two male intruders into a female society where, after copulation, they are considered as prey and killed.*

Right *Nora Kaye with Hugh Laing in Antony Tudor's ballet* Pillar of Fire, *the work which established her as a brilliant exponent of dramatic roles. As Hagar, she imagines she will lose the man she loves to her younger sister and in desperation gives herself to a stranger, but is forgiven by her real, sympathetic lover.*

Bruhn, Scott Douglas, and John Kriza starred with Kaye and the ballet, which was danced to Bartok's *Music for Strings, Percussion and Celeste*, went into the repertory. Designs were again by Geordiardis.

What was to be a lifelong friendship for Nora Kaye developed with MacMillan over this period. The second workshop performance of the season included Herbert Ross's sexually sensational adaptation of Jean Genet's *The Maids*, which MacMillan was to bring into the Royal Ballet some 14 years later when he was Director of the company, by which time Kaye and Ross were married. Tudor, de Mille, MacMillan and Ross were choreographers who fed her enthusiasm and stimulated her interpretive brilliance. In 1957 Ross created *Concerto* for her to Tchaikovsky's Violin Concerto in D; in 1958 *Dialogues* to music by Leonard Bernstein. His own career was spanning ballet and Broadway musicals (by that time *House of Flowers*, *Body Beautiful* and *Wonderful Town*) and he had choreographed the dances for the 1954 film *Carmen Jones*. Kaye's contribution to the screen at this point was to be indirectly responsible for a footnote to cinema history, when screenwriter friend Arthur Laurents, fictionalizing the story of Anna Anderson (who claimed to be Anastasia, survivor of the Russian royal family) named the Ingrid Bergman role Anna Koreff after Nora.

Ross choreographed *Angel Head* to a jazz score for Kaye to dance at the 1959 Spoleto Festival, and in 1960 she left American Ballet Theatre to form, with Ross, Ballet of Two Worlds, linked to Spoleto. She was the company's principal ballerina and created roles in two other new Ross works, *Rashomon Suite* and *The Dybbuk*.

Her marriage to Isaac Stern had been over for some years and she and Ross were married in 1960. She told friends that he proposed to her in a car at the time that Ballet of Two Worlds (for which they had had great hopes) was disbanded, and that she threw her *pointe* shoes out of the window into the river, deciding the time had come to retire from dancing.

She never looked back. She believed life should be lived in the present. She accompanied Ross to London where he worked on the choreography for two Cliff Richard films, *The Young Ones* and *Summer Holiday*. They moved their permanent base from New York—although continuing to keep an apartment in Central Park West—to Beverly Hills, as Ross's career was drawn more and more into the film industry. They lived in film star luxury and elegance, changing houses several times. Nora Kaye's flair for interior design gave her the opportunity to furnish and decorate in styles varying from Radical Chic to American Colonial, and to be able to offer a sumptuous guest suite to visiting friends who were often from the ballet. By the pool of one beautiful mansion was a wonderfully equipped gymnasium and a studio with a practise bar—a dream for hardworked dancers used to roughing it on tours. Whenever American Ballet Theatre or the Royal Ballet and other distinguished companies were performing in Los Angeles, the Rosses were always involved as friends and hosts. In later years they also owned a beach house at Malibu where they entertained more informally and with the same warm hospitality. Nora Kaye, always surrounded by a number of loved dogs, never refused to listen or help or advise her dancer friends. The girl from the Bronx could not have imagined the life that lay ahead of her.

Ross had turned to full-scale directing after working on the dance sequences of *Funny Girl*. Once again he and Kaye were based in London. This time he was directing the musical remake of *Goodbye Mr Chips* with Peter O'Toole and Petula Clark. Kaye was actively involved as the Second Unit Director—film buffs might note that there is a pillow-fight section that is hers!

From then on she was Ross's Associate Producer, and was particularly involved creatively on his three ballet films, *Nijinsky, The Turning Point* and *Giselle*, a backstage story linked to on-stage performance, with Lynn Seymour in the role of Giselle's mother. Kaye had wanted Seymour for the part of the Russian ballerina, Tamara Karsavina, in *Nijinsky*, although for various reasons it was ultimately played by the star of La Scala Ballet, Carla Fracci. Royal Ballet Principal Monica Mason danced The Chosen Maiden in MacMillan's recreation of an excerpt of Nijinsky's *Rite of Spring*, and he continued his brilliant pastiche of Nijinsky's choreographic style with a section of the 1913 ballet based on a game of tennis, *Jeux*. Nora Kaye was also instrumental in inviting ex-Ballets Russes star, Alexandra Danilova, to play her fictional counterpart in *The Turning Point*, coaching a young American dancer, Leslie Browne, in the classics.

Arthur Laurents's script was inspired by elements of Kaye's own life and the central ballerina role was indirectly based on her. When she died of cancer on 28 February 1987, Leslie Browne was quoted as saying, 'Nora Kaye was the most important influence in my whole life and I loved her.'

Browne was Kaye's god-child and had danced some of her Tudor roles with American Ballet Theatre, but other dancers also felt immense affection and gratitude. Utterly free of narcissim and jealously, Nora Kaye's support and generosity was widely acknowledged. She became a director of ABT in 1977. When it was suggested she should write her memoirs she said with characteristic lack of egotism that she would if she could only remember her memoirs. It was left for those who loved her, colleagues, friends, fans and ballet-goers, to carry their own memories of her *joie de vivre*, good humour, and outstanding talent.

R·U·D·O·L·F N·U·R·E·Y·E·V

Not since Vaslav Nijinsky first burst upon the Western world in 1909 has a male dancer had the same impact as Rudolf Nureyev. But, brilliant and beautiful as his dancing has been, his importance as an artist is outweighed by other considerations: no other male—including Nijinsky—has done so much to make the profession an acceptable one for men or, by example, done so much to raise the standard of male dancing throughout the free world. Moreover, he has been far from content to limit himself to the great classical roles or even those that have been created for him. He has had a voracious appetite to essay almost every form of theatrical dance, ranging from the title role of Glen Tetley's *Pierrot Lunaire* to Paul Taylor's *Aureole*, from the free-flowing lyricism of Jerome Robbins's *Dances at a Gathering* to Nijinsky's own stylized *L'Après-midi d'un Faune*.

But, of course, it was the combination of his impeccable classical training at the Kirov school in Leningrad allied to his own compelling on-stage presence for which he is most famous as a dancer.

Nureyev was born on a train on 17 March 1938, while his mother was on her way to join his father, a 'politruk' (a soldier whose duty it is to teach other soldiers the history of Russia, particularly the Revolution and the Communist Party) stationed in Vladivostok. She was travelling with his three elder sisters, Rosa, Rosida and Lida and was overjoyed to be able to report that, at long last, the Nureyevs had a boy.

Shortly afterwards the family moved to Moscow and then, after the outbreak of war between Russia and Germany in 1941, the family home was bombed and mother and children moved to Ufa in Bashkir, on the eastern side of the Urals. Bashkir is the area from which, Nureyev says, both sides of his family originate, the area of the Tartars, a hot-blooded, volatile race of warriors 'more languid than the Russians, a curious mixture of tenderness and brutality, sometimes cunning as a fox, a pretty complex animal . . .'

Those years of childhood in Bashkir were lived in grim poverty, the family of five sharing a small room with an elderly couple, all energy spent on foraging for food. At school the seven-year-old boy learnt Bashkir folk-songs and dances which produced in him an instant response. Home from school he would 'sing and dance until it was time to go to bed'. His inclination to dance did not go unnoticed, his mother, relations and friends all commented on it which consolidated his own conviction that his destiny was to be a dancer.

Nureyev's first encounter with classical ballet occurred when his mother contrived to get all five members of the family into the local opera house on one ticket (when the doors opened the crush and stampede was so great that

the young Nureyevs rushed past the doorman undetected) to see the Ufa Ballet Company perform a Bashkir ballet entitled *The Crane's Song*. The visit to the theatre itself was, for Rudolf, like 'visiting a palace' and the performance left him 'utterly possessed'.

At the age of 11 he met a local celebrity, a Madame Udeltsova, 70 years old who, every summer, made the trip to Leningrad to see what was happening in the arts. She was 'almost a ballet teacher', and had danced in the *corps de ballet* of Serge Diaghilev's Ballets Russes. She was impressed with young Rudolf's talent for dancing and after a year's basic study with her she recommended him to another teacher, Madame Vaitovich, who had been a soloist with the Kirov company.

During his year with Vaitovich, Nureyev heard that a number of pupils from Bashkir were going to be auditioned for the Kirov school. Nureyev was desperate to go but his father could not afford the train fare from Ufa to Leningrad. Nureyev was in 'black despair'—made all the deeper because both his parents were fiercely opposed to his desire to become a professional dancer.

Despite this parental opposition Nureyev persisted in taking secret lessons and became a major element in the school group performing national dances, which they often did in neighbouring villages. At the age of 15 he was offered the chance to play walk-on parts with the Ufa Opera Company and, on the strength of this 'position', gave lessons in folk-dance to workers' collectives, earning enough money to support himself in a frugal manner.

A year later he was offered a position in the Opera *corps de ballet*, working frantically to improve his classical technique by copying the other dancers in the daily class and at rehearsal. He was so successful that the Opera Director offered him a position as a soloist. Simultaneously, the Republic of Bashkir was selecting dancers to appear in Moscow at a festival of Bashkir art and Nureyev opted for this opportunity to appear in the capital. As it turned out an injury in rehearsal foiled his chance to dance but, using his small savings, he took the train from Moscow to Leningrad where, by a combination of luck, determination and cheek, he managed to obtain an audition for the Kirov Ballet School.

Despite his age, 17, and his lack of formal training, he was accepted as a scholarship student, paid for by the State of Bashkir.

Throughout his period as a student with the Kirov School Nureyev created

Rudolf Nureyev as Albrecht in the second act of Giselle, *the first major ballet he danced with the Royal Ballet after his defection from Russia in 1961.*

the reputation of being a rebel, a nonconformist, the difference in age and experience between himself and the other pupils being the main cause of the matter. He was particularly at odds with the Director of the School, Chelkov who, on the point of expelling Nureyev, instead maliciously placed him in the advanced class supervised by Alexander Pushkin. At first he was almost ignored by Pushkin but then, despite being technically behind the other pupils, he established a great rapport with Pushkin who, great teacher that he was, made a major contribution to Nureyev's ultimate success at the school and thus to his subsequent career.

After graduating from the school Nureyev had offers to become a soloist from both the Kirov company in Leningrad and the Bolshoi Ballet in Moscow—he was even invited to become the partner of the leading Kirov ballerina, Natalia Dudinskaya! Nureyev chose the Kirov, more aristocratic, more refined, more sophisticated than the high-powered Bolshoi company.

Throughout his period with the Kirov Ballet—notwithstanding his acknowledged brilliance as a dancer—Nureyev was looked upon, just as he had been as a student, as a maverick figure, especially as he resisted becoming a Komsomol, that is, one of the dancers concerned with the company's political relationship to the arts. He was always being denounced by (probably jealous) fellow artists and there seems to have been an official conspiracy to send him to dance at some of the coldest, most unattractive, ill-equipped and desolate parts of the Soviet Union.

Despite this situation Nureyev was part of the Kirov company that made the fateful trip to Paris in 1961 to appear at the Paris Opera. This was Nureyev's first visit to western Europe and it crystallized all his thoughts about the freedom of the artist, about political interference in the arts, about his own position within the Kirov.

When the time came for the Kirov to move on from Paris to London Nureyev was suddenly told at the airport that he was to dance in the Kremlin the following day and that he would be rejoining the company in London a couple of days after that. He knew, at that moment, that he was being sent back to the Soviet Union never to be let out again on a foreign tour. His exploratory walks in Paris, away from the official tours, his fraternization with dancers from French companies, had earned him several reprimands from the authorities; this sudden dispatch back to Russia was his punishment—a punishment that was likely to last at least as long as his career.

What happened next is now familiar history. Evading the company's Russian bodyguards, and with the assistance of Clara Saint, one of the friends he had made in Paris, Nureyev asked the French authorities for political asylum which, despite the furious arguments and blandishments put up by the Russian officials, was granted. Thus Nureyev became the first of several great Russian dancers, including Natalia Makarova and Mikhail Baryshnikov, to defect to the West.

During those first few weeks of freedom Nureyev was subjected to intense political and psychological pressure to return home. He was presented with communications from his parents (his father sent him a letter stating that he had 'betrayed the Fatherland'; his mother sent a telegram beseeching him to come home) and, just as invidiously persuasive, he received a letter from his beloved teacher Pushkin arguing that by staying in the 'decadent' West Nureyev would lose his 'moral integrity' as a dancer.

Rudolf Nureyev in the title role of Robert Helpmann's ballet Hamlet, *first produced in 1942 and revived in 1981 for the Royal Ballet's fiftieth anniversary.*

Nureyev resisted all such moral blackmail, but he also had to withstand endless interviews with members of the Western press who either asked asinine questions in pursuit of a sensational story or else wanted to make political capital out of his situation. Having made his momentous decision the aftermath, from both sides of the Iron Curtain, was difficult to endure.

Nureyev's first engagement with a Western company was with the Marquis de Cuevas' ballet company, then appearing in Paris, with Rosella Hightower, the American-born ballerina of Red Indian extraction, as his partner in the company's new production of *The Sleeping Beauty*, alternating the roles of Prince Florimund with the Blue Bird. After Paris there followed a short tour of French resorts, including Biarritz, La Baule and Deauville. After a holiday he arranged to take up a further contract, dancing with the company in Israel, Italy and Scandinavia.

During his summer interlude he went to Copenhagen, studied with the famous Russian teacher Vera Volkova, who had made her home there, and met Erik Bruhn, the great Danish *premier danseur noble*, whose dancing Nureyev much admired.

While in Denmark Nureyev received a call from Dame Margot Fonteyn, asking if he would dance at the gala she was arranging at the Theatre Royal, Drury Lane. Nureyev was happy to agree but was anxious about further sessions with members of the Western press. Fonteyn promised that he would stay with her (as the wife of Roberto de Arias, Panamanian Ambassador to the Court of St James, he would be staying at the Embassy) and that his visit would be strictly incognito. It was—Nureyev was able to wander around London's tourist sights and even take class with members of the Royal Ballet virtually unrecognized.

For the gala Nureyev danced a classical *pas de deux* with Rosella Hightower and performed a solo created specially for him by Frederick Ashton, although Nureyev chose the Scriabin music himself. The piece was called *Poème Tragique* which some critics imagined referred to his decision to leave his homeland but which, in fact, had nothing to do with reality. All the critics, and the gala audience, raved about his dazzling dancing and for London as well as Paris he had become an overnight megastar of the dance.

Following the conclusion of his contract with the de Cuevas company, which ended in Venice in midwinter, Nureyev made a number of guest appearances in Europe, including Munich and Vienna, and also on television. Together with Erik Bruhn, Sonia Arova and Maria Tallchief he formed a quartet to give chamber performances for a short season in Paris. Then Bruhn sustained an injury and Nureyev had to take over his roles at short notice—including a commission to appear on American television. This was Nureyev's introduction to the United States but, apart from the TV performance and two guest appearances with Ruth Page's company in New York his stay there was more of a holiday. While in that city he saw the New York City Ballet performing works by George Balanchine and Jerome Robbins and met both choreographers.

However, this was an uneasy period; Nureyev was still a celebrity mainly through his defection rather than his dancing, although most of the ballet world had heard of his prowess and was agog to see him. But he was a dancer without a company, a traveller without a home.

Dame Ninette de Valois, Director of the Royal Ballet, was determined that this brilliant young Russian should perform with the company, confident that, apart from his obvious box-office attraction, Nureyev's superb Kirov training could only have a beneficial influence on the soloists and principals of Britain's national company. Thus began Nureyev's first engagement with the Royal Ballet, partnering Margot Fonteyn in three performances of *Giselle*. It was the regular London audience's first chance to see him in a full-length role and the impact of his dancing was stupendous. His beautiful classical technique, the vibrant athleticism of his jumps, his passionate intensity in the role of Albrecht, came as a revelation of what male dancing could be—especially in a ballet that can so often seem no more than an exquisite museum piece, a lovely relic of nineteenth-century Romanticism. Nureyev's commitment made the work relevant to modern audiences.

Those performances of *Giselle* also marked the beginning of Nureyev's famous partnership with Margot Fonteyn—two artists who, despite the difference in their ages, complemented each other marvellously on-stage, he with a virile masculinity, she with classical purity and grace, both of them superb exemplars of the classical style.

Merely to catalogue Nureyev's progress through the world of dance would need a book of some length but, at the outset of his career in the West there is no doubt that, despite the world-wide demand for his services as a guest artist, his partnership with Fonteyn was of paramount importance. Moreover, his frequent appearances with the Royal Ballet (his status as a foreign subject prevented him becoming a member of the company) as a 'permanent guest artist', gave him a firm base in a company of international standing with considerable resources. London, indeed, became his home base and he bought a large, rambling house near Richmond Park as well as a villa on the French Riviera.

Everything Nureyev did, everywhere he went, was headline news. On his first visit to Canada, dancing with the Royal Ballet, he was taken to a police

Right *Rudolf Nureyev in the title role of Balanchine's* The Prodigal Son, *first produced for Serge Diaghilev's Ballets Russes in 1929, with a score by Serge Prokofiev and decor by Georges Rouault.*

Left *Rudolf Nureyev in the virtuoso solo from the* Le Corsaire pas de deux.

station for crossing the road without heeding the traffic lights; he was knocked down by a motor scooter in Chelsea and just avoided serious injury; he was rehearsing with Fonteyn when she received news that her husband had been badly wounded in an assassination attempt; he had his tonsils removed in a London clinic; together with Fonteyn he was arrested in San Francisco after a tip-off that they might be taking drugs at a party; he threw a salad at a celebrated critic in Australia. It was all grist to the mill of gossip columnists and it has continued throughout his career.

But it has been Nureyev's achievements as a dancer, a choreographer, a director and a film actor that has produced the real news.

In 1962 Nureyev appeared in Paul Czinner's film *An Evening with the Royal Ballet*. In 1963, with Fonteyn, he danced his first created role in Ashton's *Marguerite and Armand*. That same year he danced in his own first production, Act III of *La Bayadère* for the Royal Ballet. In 1964 he reconstructed the full-length *Raymonda* for the Royal Ballet touring company (now Sadler's Wells Royal Ballet). In 1966 he choreographed his first work, *Tancredi*, for the Vienna Opera Ballet. In the same year Roland Petit created *Paradise Lost* for Nureyev and Fonteyn, for the Royal Ballet. Also that year they danced in the film version of Kenneth MacMillan's *Romeo and Juliet*. In 1968 he gave his first performance in a modern dance work, *Monument for a Dead Boy*, created for the Dutch National Ballet by Rudi van Dantzig. In 1970 he danced the leading role in van Dantzig's *Ropes of Time*, created for the Royal Ballet. In 1972 he directed the film of his own production of *Don Quixote* for the Australian Ballet. In 1976 he appeared in the title role of Ken Russell's film *Rudolph Valentino*. All the time, in between creating new ballets and working in films and on television, he was dancing all over the world with classical and modern companies, large and small. Usually the performances were brilliant and spectacular, sometimes they were controversial, frequently he was mis-cast but always his dancing was absorbing and interesting, always his presence filled the theatre to overflowing.

Several of Nureyev's stagings of the classics have been splendid, including *Swan Lake* for the Vienna Opera Ballet, *The Nutcracker* for the Royal Ballet, *Raymonda* and *Don Quixote* for the Australian Ballet and *The Sleeping Beauty* for the Canadian National Ballet and London Festival Ballet. His original works with his own choreography cannot be accounted so successful. For example his lengthy, ambitious staging of *Romeo and Juliet* for London Festival Ballet, although it has several clever theatrical effects, fails at the crucial *pas de deux* for the lovers, where the choreography becomes fussy and awkward.

Likewise, his one-act *Manfred*, based on the programmatic symphony by

B·A·L·L·E·T G·E·N·I·U·S

Tchaikovsky, for London Festival Ballet in 1979, and *The Tempest*, using various Tchaikovsky scores, for the Royal Ballet in 1982, although possessing undeniable moments of theatricality, cannot be considered choreographically successful and have not been retained in the repertoires.

In 1983 Nureyev became Director of the Paris Opera Ballet, the oldest classical company in the world and one of the most prestigious, but also with a reputation for Byzantine politics, with backstage factions constantly at odds, with a dance hierarchy guarded with fanatical jealousy, with endless quarrels between artists and administration . . . Nureyev, with his own volatile temperament and reputation for 'scenes', would seem to be the ideal person to govern the ungovernable. Certainly, his regime there, albeit controversial, has been undeniably progressive and has produced a number of interesting seasons including a programme of ballets by the late Antony Tudor and a full-length version of *Cinderella* set in Hollywood!

Throughout this time Nureyev has kept dancing. During the late seventies there was a noticeable decline in his technical ability and several of his performances were frankly disappointing. For a number of people his continuing attempts to dance roles for which he no longer possesses the stamina and technique have been sad occasions, tending to obscure the memory of his great performances at the height of his physical powers. But he is driven to dance and his presence on the bill will still secure a box-office sell-out irrespective of the quality of his dancing.

For nearly 30 years Nureyev has been a major star not just of the ballet but in several of the performance arts. His name is a household word, his physical presence—whether on-stage, film or television—is compelling. But it is his monumental contribution to the status of male dancing in the West that his importance will be judged in years to come.

In November, 1987, Nureyev was at last allowed back into the Soviet Union to see his ailing mother and his sister. It was an emotional reunion, very private, although, of course, the world's press were in attendance. The question they were asking, however, was 'Will Nureyev dance again in Russia? Will he be taking the Paris Opera Company there on a visit?' Only time—and *glasnost*—will tell.

'Miss Peggy Hookham was easily the hit of the performance.' When Hilda Hookham read her daughter's first public notice in a Shanghai paper she decided the time had come to take the child's dancing more seriously and removed her from Madame Tarakanova who had staged the show. Madame lost her pupil but gained an entry in the history books as teacher to the youthful Margot Fonteyn.

Madame Tarakanova was not Fonteyn's first teacher. Several years earlier, in the west London suburb of Ealing, she had attended Miss Grace Bosustow's Academy for dancing lessons and there made her first stage appearance as the 'Wind' in a ballet for tiny tots. She was seven years old when, leaving her elder brother Felix at school in England, she accompanied her parents to the East. Her father, also called Felix, was an engineer working for the British Cigarette Company, a subsidiary of The British American Tobacco Company, and he had been offered the post of Chief Engineer at the company's works in Shanghai. On 12 April 1928 the family arrived in China by way of the United States.

Peggy was happy enough in her new environment although she badly missed her brother. If the family had been temporarily severed however, the life-style continued. There is a photograph of a corner of the Shanghai drawing-room which, apart from an oriental lampshade with a bamboo print, might still be in Ealing. On the sofa sits Mr Hookham in suit and tie, Peggy on his right holding an open book, Hilda on his left taking something (a chocolate perhaps?) from a box on the piano stool. The three faces project one forward to the much photographed face of the grown Margot Fonteyn. At 11 her familiar features were concealed by the rounded contours of extreme youth but they are there in the parents, strongly inherited. Hilda, of mixed Brazilian and Irish descent was dark-haired and remarkably attractive and was a formative if not forceful influence on her daughter's career (and there are many contemporary ballet-goers who will recall her in the audience at her daughter's performances until Fonteyn's retirement in 1979). Her decision to take Peggy out of Madame Tarakanova's classes and transfer her to the Russian trainer George Gontcharov was to change their lives.

Fate brings unlikely people together in unlikely places with unimagined consequences. Gontcharov had left Russia to open his school in Shanghai in the 1920s and among his pupils was June Bear who was to become June Brae, two years older than Peggy Hookham and already demonstrating striking talent. June's mother played the piano for the lessons and, as is the way with 'ballet mothers' the two ex-patriots discussed the future of their girls. When June and her mother left for England, June to study with the renowned Nicholas Legat

who had recently established a school in London, Mrs Hookham was inspired to make a similar decision and followed with Peggy, arranging for her to train with Serafine Astafieva.

Astafieva was a princess as well as being a dancer and teacher, and she lived on the first floor of a house called The Pheasantry at 152 King's Road, Chelsea. There she had taught Anton Dolin and Alicia Markova and now the 13-year-old Peggy Hookham. (Later the basement of the house became a famous arts club, and the facade still remains inspite of redevelopment, graced by a blue plaque of commemoration.) Perhaps it was at the suggestion of this esteemed teacher that Peggy also took lessons at the (then) Vic-Wells School. It was the aim of all aspiring ballerinas to be taken into an established company while they were still young, or rather, in this case, the aim of the aspiring mother, for Peggy, apparently, had no desire for it. Inwardly rebellious although outwardly acquiescent, she accompanied her mother to Islington where the school was housed in the Sadler's Wells theatre. She was rather overwhelmed by the organization and what at first seemed a confusion of dancers, teachers and pupils. She was 14, reserved and shy. William Chappell, dancing with the company, found her a 'rather annoyingly self-possessed child' and was quite surprised when Ninette de Valois drew his attention to her. 'That child', said de Valois decisively, 'has talent.'

A year later 'that child' was taken into the company. She was now calling herself Margot Fontes, taking her mother's maiden name, but de Valois changed it to Fonteyn. She is reputed to have said, 'At last we have found and created a real British ballerina. For heaven's sake don't let her sound Spanish!' She also said, and this is recorded fact from de Valois herself, 'We must do something about saving those feet.' She had been trained by Edouard Espinosa who never allowed his pupils to go home after class in ordinary shoes, but insisted on boots (laced or buttoned in those days) to support the ankles. This she passed on to Fonteyn who many years later recalled the advice and found that contemporary boots were just as effective.

The newest company recruits frequently made their débuts in *The Nutcracker*, and Margot Fonteyn, approximately a decade after her first stage role of the 'Wind' at Bosustow's Academy, graduated to 'Snowflake' at Sadler's Wells. The Sugar Plum Fairy was Alicia Markova, Fonteyn's ideal of a ballerina, unique, brilliant and impossible to emulate. The humble snowflake watched, enchanted,

Margot Fonteyn as Nikiya in Nureyev's production of the third act of La Bayadère *by Marius Petipa.*

privileged to share the stage. Fonteyn was just 15, Markova 23.

Once again Fonteyn appeared with Markova in Ninette de Valois's *The Haunted Ballroom*, a highly dramatic and romantic three-act ballet in which the doomed hero dances to death with the ghosts in his own ballroom. The characters were named after the dancers who created them, and in later years, when Markova had left the company, 'Alicia' was danced by Fonteyn. In the minor role of the Young Treginnis 'Fonteyn struck me as good' said William Chappell who danced a major role, 'no *better* . . . as any of her forerunners.'

About this time June Brae (née Bear) joined her old Shanghai classmate in the company, having been picked out by de Valois from the chorus at The London Coliseum. With June from her past among the company girls, there was among the contemporary boys one who would partner Fonteyn in the illustrious future, Michael Somes. Also with Sadler's Wells was the young man who would shape her career even more than de Valois, the choreographer Frederick Ashton whose muse she became.

The first Ashton role Fonteyn performed was the Creole Girl in *Rio Grande*, originally danced by Markova. The part was not important but it was effective in a work which was ahead of its time, although it did not remain in the repertoire. Only the astute de Valois would have given the role to a dancer as inexperienced as the 16-year-old Fonteyn, but with that judgement of potential proven again and again during her directorship of the company, she knew that she had here Markova's likely successor. Against Edward Burra's brilliant tropical backdrop, Fonteyn gave a vibrant and lively performance. Later she was to admit that she enjoyed it because she did not have to wear *pointe* shoes. There were no nerve-racking arabesques!

Ashton created his first role for Fonteyn in 1935, the Fianceé in *Le Baiser de la fée*. Based on the Hans Christian Anderson story *The Ice Maiden*, to a Stravinsky score, the ballet had been choreographed before by Bronislava Nijinska for Ida Rubinstein's company in Paris. Ashton had been a member of that company, and now decided to prepare his own version for Sadler's Wells. Markova had just left the company and Fonteyn had enlarged her repertoire within the classics and with contemporary works like Ashton's charming and amusing suite of dances, *Les Rendezvous*. She was not yet dancing principal roles (there were four or five dancers amongst whom these were divided) but she was ostensibly being groomed. *Baiser* was an important step on the way. With the beautiful Pearl Argyle as the Fairy, audiences that November revelled in the knowledge that the Russians were at last being challenged by British ballet and British dancers.

Fonteyn's development was not under the same pressure as it would be today. The Sadler's Wells season ran from the end of September until the beginning of May, but during that time there were only two performances a week. Between each season the company toured for seven weeks, and everyone enjoyed a long summer vacation. She worked tirelessly at her craft and was nagged by her elders for wearing old *pointe* shoes because she found them more comfortable. 'Those feet' again!

Apparitions, Ashton's next work for Fonteyn, was hailed as a triumph. Constant Lambert, Musical Director of the Company, arranged the Liszt score and Cecil Beaton contributed romantic designs. The leading male role was danced by Robert Helpmann in the high Gothick mood of the earlier *Haunted Ballroom*, and Fonteyn was acclaimed as the Woman in a Balldress.

She was established now as a ballerina. By 1937 she had danced Odette (with Ruth French as Odile) in *Swan Lake*, and her *Giselle*, performed for once by a girl of the correct age, was remarkable for its youthful poignancy. As she took her curtain-calls after what can only be described as a marathon achievement, there was nothing to indicate that she had been out dancing until 4 a.m. that morning. In later years she looked back on her naïvety with some astonishment. 'I was nervous . . . because it is always alarming to perform, but then it was only a straightforward case of nerves.' Ever afterwards she went to bed as early as possible on the night before a *Giselle*. Each time, she said, 'my nightmares become more frightening'.

That same year she added to her repertoire two other Ashton roles, in *Les Patineurs*, his delightful skating *divertissement*, and *A Wedding Bouquet*, that highly *avant garde* work with music and décor by Lord Berners and words by Gertrude Stein spoken over the score. (In the latter Ninette de Valois created her own final role as a dancer.)

In June, at the end of the Sadler's Wells season, the company was invited to Paris for the great Exhibition of industry and art. The Theatre de Champs-Elysée was the centre for the various visiting international companies, and the sense of pride among the English dancers was temporarily shattered by the discovery that no one had put up their posters. As a result the first night was poorly attended, but the critics were tremendously enthusiastic for a repertoire of five Ashton ballets, de Valois's *The Rake's Progress* and the première of her *Checkmate*. This was Fonteyn's first real experience of the city she was to grow to love and return to again and again. While mature members of the company were in Pigalle until dawn, Mrs Hookham saw to it that her daughter behaved rather more decorously, which caused one dancer (with *Checkmate* in mind)

Right Margot Fonteyn in the grand pas *from* Pacquita *by Marius Petipa, staged for a Royal Academy of Dancing gala in 1964 by Rudolf Nureyev.*

Left Margot Fonteyn with Rudolf Nureyev in the second act of Giselle, *the first major ballet in which they appeared with the Royal Ballet in 1962.*

to refer to her unkindly as the Black Queen. Whether she accompanied Fonteyn on tour later that summer is not on record. In Cambridge where the company was booked for a week, the young soloist's constant companion was a dark-haired, good-looking undergraduate from Panama, Roberto (Tito) de Arias.

The company moved on to the next town and the summer holiday followed. For a time, apparently, Margot and Tito kept in contact but eventually they lost touch. Their lives were increasingly busy, the war intervened, he married and had children. Both however remembered the happy week in Cambridge with tender feelings.

The September season began. Fonteyn danced with Somes in a revival of Ashton's *Pomona* and in a new, redesigned production of *Les Rendezvous*. On 21 December she danced the full role of Odette/Odile in *Swan Lake*. In January Ashton's *Horoscope* was premièred. The part of The Young Woman (Sun in Virgo, Moon in Gemini) was danced by Fonteyn with Michael Somes (Sun in Leo, Moon in Gemini) as her partner. There was a mixed reaction from the critics, and one horribly memorable night when Somes's mesh shirt somehow became entangled in Fonteyn's flowing costume at the climax of a glorious *pas de deux*, and they were forced to improvize their exit. (The score by Constant Lambert was dedicated to Fonteyn and was, alas, lost for ever in 1940 in Holland when the Nazis invaded and the company, on tour, had to make a hasty departure.)

Fonteyn had danced Aurora in February 1939, with June Brae as the Lilac Fairy and Robert Helpmann as Prince Florimund, and this significant production of *The Sleeping Princess* was the last of the classics to be performed before the outbreak of hostilities. The company was in Leeds in September when war was declared and de Valois immediately disbanded her dancers, only to reform them two weeks later in Cardiff, with a small repertoire, no orchestra and not much money. By the end of the year the postponed season at Sadler's Wells was under way, with Fonteyn in a new Ashton work, *Dante Sonata*, a moving statement on the horror and pointless devastation of war which stunned audiences with its potent message.

On 4 May the company left London and travelled to neutral Holland on a small Dutch vessel, and having docked, were transported by bus to The Hague, the central point for their ten-day tour. The reality of war resulted in a fraught journey back to England, a temporary base at The New Theatre (now the Albery) in St Martin's Lane and the decimation of the company as one male dancer after another was called up. Throughout the duration Fonteyn toured the length and breadth of the country, taking on an arduous schedule in scaled-down versions of the classics and a modern repertoire, living in London with her mother in the short breaks between tours. With all the deprivations and anxieties, there was the additional fears for her father, arrested and eventually interned by the Japanese when they invaded mainland China.

All this took its toll, both physically and emotionally, and Fonteyn felt her technique also suffered. In 1945, shortly before the end of the war, the company returned to the New Theatre. There was then a 10-week tour for the armed forces in Germany and in 1946 Fonteyn began to take private lessons with Vera Volkova, the leading teacher of the contemporary classical style who had recently started teaching in London. Fonteyn found the lessons of immense help in preparing for the splendid new production of *The Sleeping Beauty* which was to re-open the Royal Opera House, used as a dance-hall during the war. Equally important, this was the production which would establish the Sadler's Wells Ballet as the resident company. It is astonishing, now, to realize that they had danced there only twice before, in 1933, as the Camargo Society, and at a Gala in 1939.

The night was a high point in theatre history. Fonteyn and Helpmann, who had danced together in the 1939 production of *The Sleeping Princess* appeared again as Aurora and her Prince, only now Helpmann doubled in the travesty role of Carabosse, the wicked fairy. Ashton had devised some new arrangements and felicitous additions, and Oliver Messell designed the brilliant costumes and décor, a glorious visual feast after the austerity years.

It was Fonteyn's performance as Princess Aurora that crystallized, both for critics and for audiences, those qualities that had so inspired Ashton to create roles for her during the thirties and which he was to continue to do until her final appearances in ballerina roles in the late seventies. Fonteyn was Ashton's muse for some 40 years.

Fonteyn was never a virtuoso performer—or, rather, her virtuosity was hidden by a seemingly effortless grace and poise, the perfect example of the art that conceals art. Virtuosity, *per se*, would have seemed, for her, mere vulgarity; in her performances it was the technical means by which she would find the truth, the centre, the heart of a characterization. In the role of Aurora, for example, she would appear a radiantly happy young girl on her sixteenth birthday, greeting her parents and the Princes who had come to court with an unaffected charm, never a ballerina about to tackle a famous *adage*.

Yet it is perfectly possible to analyse her technique: it was, quite simply, classical perfection. A purity of line, a precision in placement, every movement exquisitely phrased and performed with flawless musicality. Which is not to say that there were not moments of excitement, of an exultation in execution that added something special to bravura passages, from the *grand pas de deux* of *The Sleeping*

Beauty to the *manège* of pirouettes that expressed Chloe's joy at her reunion with Daphnis. These were qualities that made Fonteyn the Royal Ballet's only officially designated *prima ballerina assoluta* to date.

Later in that opening season at Covent Garden in 1946, on 24 April, came another of those theatrical peaks, the première of Ashton's *Symphonic Variations* which, with *The Sleeping Beauty,* has become a signature work of the company.

Symphonic Variations, to Cesar Franck's score and with a masterpiece décor by Sophie Fedorovitch contributing to the perfect simplicity of the whole, used six dancers in a manner that epitomized the lyrical classicism that Ashton had developed. It was the distillation of 'the English style', a wonderful synthesis of music, movement and design. The original cast, which many believe has never been surpassed, was Pamela May, Moira Shearer and Margot Fonteyn with Michael Somes, Henry Danton and Brian Shaw.

Almost exactly two years later Fonteyn was in Paris in the première of Roland Petit's ballet about cats, *Les Demoiselles de la Nuit.* This work, together with Ashton's *Scènes de Ballet,* in which she and Somes were the principal couple, gave her, according to one critic, new authority and the understanding of 'elegance rather than mere *chic*.' It is worth noting that *Scènes de Ballet* is considered one of Ashton's masterpieces. His next work, *Don Juan,* was less successful, and Fonteyn tore a ligament on the opening night, which meant that not only could she not dance other performances but she was also out of *Cinderella,* which he was creating for her, until later in the season. Moira Shearer replaced her, but Fonteyn's eventual interpretation drew great praise. Mary Clark wrote that she was 'not afraid to look a drab and frightened waif . . . (which) lent her transformation an added radiance'. (Fonteyn continued to dance the role with the Royal Ballet until 1965.)

Fonteyn was still taking class with Vera Volkova only days before the company left for its very first American season. They opened at the Metropolitan Opera on 9 October 1949, with Margot Fonteyn and Robert Helpmann in *The Sleeping Beauty.* Ashton was Carabosse and Beryl Grey the Lilac Fairy and the orchestra was conducted by Constant Lambert. It was an overwhelming success and Fonteyn was extolled as the *prima ballerina assoluta* of the company by audiences ready to take a star to their hearts. There is always a reticence to respond in the British psyche, but New York openly adored her, although not sufficiently to praise *Symphonic Variations* which had been such a hit at home. 'Watered down Balanchine' was the consensus, 'dancing in a vacuum'. It took many years for them to recognize its worth.

The following September the company again set off on an American tour, this time taking de Valois's last major ballet, *Don Quixote* with Fonteyn in the dual role of Dulcinea-Aldonza and Helpmann as Don Quixote. Reviews in England had been divided. America did not like it at all, although Fonteyn came in for some plaudits. *Dante Sonata* was also in the repertoire and got short shrift, altogether a less enthusiastic reception than the previous year.

Back home, Ashton started work on his version of *Daphnis and Chloe* for Fonteyn and Somes, to music by Ravel and designs by John Craxton, the brilliant young English painter who lived in Greece. Curiously this time it was the Americans, during the 1953 tour, who hailed it as a masterpiece while the British had been less than lukewarm. Ashton himself, despite subsequent performances by other ballerinas, has always missed Fonteyn in the role of the shepherdess Chloe, the perfect interpretor of his concept.

It was on that visit to New York that Roberto de Arias, the student she had met in Cambridge 16 years previously, turned up in her dressing-room heralded by a bunch of red roses. He was the Panamanian consul to the United Nations and the severed relationship was back on course. The courtship was so discreet that even the eagle-eyed gossip journalists were taken by surprise. Close friends had respected her privacy and the wedding on 7 February 1955 hit the world headlines. They were married in Paris, Fonteyn wearing a plain grey taffeta dress designed by Dior who made most of her clothes. Because 'Tito' had been married before, it was a civil service at the Panamanian consulate, performed in Spanish. Among the witnesses was Dame Ninette and among the guests at a hotel off the Champs-Elysées, members of the Sadler's Wells Ballet.

The honeymoon in the Bahamas was short. Fonteyn had to be back at the Opera House for rehearsals, but was not to be separated from her husband who was shortly to take up his appointment as Panamanian Ambassador to the Court of St James. The evening after her return she gave a party on stage for the company and the Opera House staff, electricians, stage-hands, programme-sellers et al. From now on she encompassed a second career as an active ambassadorial hostess, and in acknowledgement of her first, de Arias sent her red roses at each performance.

The 1950s were an extraordinary decade for Margot Fonteyn. In 1956 she was made a Dame of the British Empire. While she continued to perform the great nineteenth-century classics, Ashton had added to her repertoire with *Sylvia*, *Homage to the Queen* (his Coronation tribute to Elizabeth II), *Birthday Offering* (in celebration of the twenty-fifth anniversary of the company's formation) and *Ondine*, his first full-length ballet based on the Giradoux play about a water-sprite in love with a mortal. The score was commissioned from the German

Above Margot Fonteyn as Princess Aurora in The Sleeping Beauty, *one of the roles closely associated with this most famous of British ballerinas.*

Right Margot Fonteyn in the Shadow Dance from Frederick Ashton's ballet Ondine.

composer Hans Werner Henze and the designs from Lila de Nobile. There were visual theatrical effects from both the designs and the choreography, but the score was generally found to be unimaginative and disappointing and the scenario insufficiently explicit. Fonteyn's central performance was a personal triumph and an artistic success, so much so that when she could no longer dance it, it was dropped from the repertory until a revival in 1988.

The watery world of *Ondine* had an extraordinary real-life counterpart when, in the late spring of 1959, newspaper headlines declaimed that Dame Margot Fonteyn de Arias was fleeing in a launch on the Pacific, accused of conspiracy in a Central American revolution. She was arrested, questioned and released. In the whole comic-opera shambles various stories circulated; that she had been aware of the Castro revolution before the British Diplomatic Service; that de Arias had led a plot to overthrow the Panamanian government and was foiled. It was an unlikely backdrop for a British ballerina. A year or so later he was re-appointed to Great Britain as Ambassador, by which time Rudolf Nureyev had defected to the West and Fonteyn was to embark on another phase of her career.

She was organizing a gala for the Royal Academy of Dancing at Drury Lane and decided to invite Nureyev to take part. He was in Vera Volkova's flat in Copenhagen when she telephoned to ask him, and perhaps her recent experience in subterfuge prompted her to suggest the initial visit should be kept secret. He had been hounded by the media and she understood his reticence to face the battery of reporters and cameras. She was an essentially private person herself.

He stayed with her at the Embassy. 'From the first moment,' he said, 'I knew I had found a friend.' She took him round incognito, introducing him as a student, even sneaked him into a Royal Ballet class. After five days he returned to Paris, arriving back in London in time to rehearse a solo choreographed for him by Ashton and on 2 November 1961 he made his British debut in the work set to Scriabine's *Poème Tragique*. Two months later he was back in London rehearsing *Giselle* with Fonteyn. 'From the first,' he wrote 'I found that I could work with Margot in complete understanding. Though she was a great ballerina with enormous experience she accepted my attitude as though we were on the same level. She did not agree to everything. There was no question of English politeness or condescension.'

Nureyev was 24, Fonteyn over 40, but the artistic rapport between them was demonstrated at those three performances of *Giselle* to rapturous audiences who had queued, begged, bribed and overpaid for tickets. Fonteyn's Giselle, partnered for so long by Somes, and latterly by David Blair, was familiar and much loved and admired. With the young Russian partner there was a renaissance that was to grow and blossom and, as Dame Ninette de Valois so succinctly described it, gave a 'face-lift' to the Royal Ballet.

In 1963 Frederick Ashton choreographed *Marguerite and Armand* for them, based on the novel by Alexander Dumas, *La Dame aux Camélias*, and it was not unusual to see fans sleeping all night in Floral Street, Covent Garden, in order to be at the box-office when it opened. Romantically set by Cecil Beaton, passionate, heart-rending, dramatic, tragic, handkerchiefs were out in the Opera House. It turned out, as David Vaughan, Ashton's biographer, has pointed out, to be Ashton's ultimate homage to Fonteyn, his last complete ballet for her. In it she demonstrated her gifts both as an actress and a dancer, and her power to touch the emotions of her audiences. The partnership of Nureyev and Fonteyn extended beyond balletomania and achieved the kind of public recognition reserved for film-stars like Astaire and Rogers.

There were similar all-night queues when they danced Kenneth MacMillan's *Romeo and Juliet* in 1965. In fact MacMillan had created the roles on Lynn Seymour and Christopher Gable, but such was the mesmeric power of the two ballet superstars that Sol Hurok, the impresario who presented the Royal Ballet in New York, insisted that they should dance the world première in London in order to promote the work in the United States. The Opera House management acquiesced, the public was unaware of the behind-scenes personal dramas and Fonteyn and Nureyev received 43 curtain-calls. It was a triumph for everyone involved. 'Juliet is Margot Fonteyn's greatest role', declared the *Los Angeles Times*, echoing the press throughout the American tour. Together Fonteyn and Nureyev were fêted and interviewed and pursued, and Fonteyn was involved in yet another headline chase when she fled over the rooftops following a drugs raid on a private party at which she and Nureyev were guests. 'Ballerina Busted' said the media, and speculated ridiculously whether the elegant ambassadorial wife had become part of the Swinging Sixties.

She seemed to be courted by drama and ultimately by tragic drama when her husband, standing for election in Panama, was shot in an assassination attempt and left paralysed and speechless.

Roberto de Arias was transferred from his own country to Stoke Mandeville Hospital in Oxfordshire. Doing her best to keep out of the limelight, Fonteyn commuted between there and London while she continued her work with the company. It was two and a half years before he was sufficiently recovered to return to Panama where, after her retirement, Fonteyn was to join him permanently.

Among the new works now created for her was John Cranko's *Poème de l'Extase* in which an ageing diva spurns her young lover and remembers the admirers of her youth. The costumes by Jurgen Rose after the Viennese painter Klimpt were romantic and flattering as was the work itself, which suited her with its graceful lifts and expressive movements. She continued to dance it until her retirement on her sixtieth birthday in May 1979, when a special gala was held in her honour at the Royal Opera House. In it she performed the tango from Ashton's *Facade*, with Helpmann as her partner, and *Salut d'amour* which Ashton had choreographed for the occasion, a gentle piece in which she was quite beautiful. The men of the Royal Ballet then presented her, each in turn, with a rose, and those fortunate enough to be in the house that evening recalled past performances and thanked her with tears of nostalgia and gratitude.

'I hope I am more than a pair of trained feet.' When David Wall spoke those words he was still a principal of the Royal Ballet. He was to remain with the company for another 10 years before retiring in 1984 to become Director of the Royal Academy of Dancing. He left before the inevitable decline of physical energy and at the height of his dramatic prowess, a decision that other great artists have not always had the strength to make. It was in keeping with the pragmatic approach to all the challenges in a brilliant, hardworking career.

'If the artist has an intelligent reason for his function, then it must be to communicate something of the miracle of a human being. That is the only reason that could make a grown man, in his senses, devote his life to the theatre.' David Wall is essentially a man of the theatre, and far more than that pair of trained feet. He combines intelligence and heart. From the outset of his professional life he imbued the smallest character role with motivation. He had been in the company only a short time when the critic Clive Barnes observed that the Persian Prince supporting Aurora in the famous, difficult *Rose Adagio* sequence in *The Sleeping Beauty*, gave substance to a part that is generally nothing more than a prop. The scene takes place on the princess's sixteenth birthday. The King has invited four suitors from whom she is to choose a husband, and in turn each hands her a rose. On this occasion David Wall watched her every movement and invested the moment when he handed her the rose with the emotional sensitivity of a man in love by caressing the flower as he did so.

David Wall's interest in the theatre was encouraged early in his dancing career by John Field, director of the touring arm of the Royal Ballet, who became something of a mentor. It was Paul Scofield in *Timon of Athens* who made Wall aware that an actor can hold and manipulate an audience and David, still in his teens, realized he wanted that kind of power and drama to characterize his own work on stage.

There was nothing theatrical in his background. He says his family did not even go to the theatre. His father was transport manager of an engineering firm that made diesel engines, and the Walls with three adopted children—David came in the middle between Josephine and Barbara, all five years apart—lived in Staines, Middlesex, a dormitory town now on the edge of Heathrow Airport. David attended a private school where ballroom dancing was part of the curriculum for the five-year-olds. 'I used to waltz my little partners about to the gramophone.' The dancing teacher, Miss Durnford, had a ballet school in Windsor and she persuaded Mrs Wall to bring David to the Saturday morning class. His aptitude was such that she entered him for the Royal Academy of Dancing grade examinations which he passed, and at the age of eight he joined

an 'Associates' class at Sadler's Wells Ballet School which subsequently became the Royal Ballet School, when the company was granted the Royal Charter in 1956. He attended twice a week, often arriving sick from the bus ride into London.

He accepted dancing as an unexceptional part of his life. He was never pressurized, and is convinced that if he had wanted to give it up, no one would have tried to make him do otherwise. He enjoyed athletics generally, and accepted ballet training as an extension of gymnastics and games. He thinks the boys at school were unaware of his double life, he was certainly never teased or ragged about it. He still had not seen a live ballet production, but at seven saw a performance on television. His own acting was confined to a certain dexterity with glove puppets and a school version of The Snow Queen in which he forgot his lines.

He was 10 when he was taken as a day boy at White Lodge, the junior school of the (now) Royal Ballet School. This was the year the school moved to the lovely premises in Richmond Park, and for three years David made the long bus journey until it was arranged for him to become a boarder. He was never homesick, perhaps because of the continuity of his teachers, Sarah Payne and Errol Addison, strong influences in his development. Addison was very much a 'man's teacher', working on turns and jumps. Wall wishes there had been the opportunity to play a musical instrument, but at White Lodge there was no time to teach anything but a sound grounding in theory. With a full academic curriculum and dancing the days were crammed.

Twice a term the pupils were taken to Covent Garden to see the company, and two ballets, John Cranko's *Antigone* and Frederick Ashton's *La Fille mal gardée* convinced the 14-year-old David Wall that he really did want to be a dancer. In particular, David Blair's performance in *Fille* as the dashing young farmhand, Colas, demonstrated the possibility of real characterization, and a style of male dancing that was more appealing than the rather vapid princes in the classics.

At 16, Wall graduated to the Upper School in Baron's Court, West London, where the Royal Ballet company rehearsed on the same premises, and there he was able to watch the recently arrived Rudolph Nureyev, who was to enhance the image of the male dancer, and the legendary Margot Fonteyn. It was beyond the stretch of Wall's imagination that he would one day partner her.

He had made his first appearance on the Opera House stage when he was still at White Lodge, during the annual Royal Ballet School matinée. He had

David Wall as Prince Siegfried in Swan Lake. *A dancer with unrivalled histrionic ability he also possessed an exemplary classical style.*

been one of 10 boys performing a stylized gymnastic display, innovative in 1961, but now a regular item. Dame Ninette de Valois had suggested it as a way of further changing the public perception of the male ballet dancer, to be seen as muscular and athletic as a footballer, but considerably more controlled.

In March 1963, some of the senior students of the school took part in a Royal Ballet gala. Ashton's *Marguerite and Armand*, his version of *Camille*, received its première that night, but the evening began with the students performing extracts from Roland Petit's quirky *Ballabile* (Wall was a pierrot) which flopped. Three months later he made a marked success in *Motus*, created especially for the Royal Ballet School Matinée by Miro Zoltan to Britten's Variations and Fugue on a Theme of Purcell. The event was also remarkable for the inclusion of another star of the future, Jennifer Penney.

Still a student, Wall danced with the resident company before it set off on a long American tour. The Royal Ballet touring company then embarked on a season at the Opera House, and he was brought in whenever an additional dancer was required. At the end of this season, the director, John Field, offered him a contract, before the resident company returned. He was not yet 17. Alfreda Thorogood, who was to become his wife, was already in the company.

Sadler's Wells Ballet had, on receiving its Royal Charter, become the Royal Ballet, and had been split into two distinct companies. The resident company was at the Opera House, and the touring company had scaled-down productions suitable for small provincial theatres. It was generally called 'the second company' but David Wall insists that second did not mean second-rate. His very first professional engagement was in Wolverhampton, where he was the Persian Prince in the *Rose Adagio*, singled out for praise by Clive Barnes. In the same evening he was also a Cavalier in the Prologue and Florestan in the *pas de trois divertissement* at Aurora's wedding in *The Sleeping Beauty's* final act.

In those days Wall's life was divided between landladies and digs while on tour, and sharing a flat with John Ryder, a Royal Ballet School friend when in London. Unlike the later years in the main company, there was constant opportunity to perform. He found it a continual learning experience. If something did not go right one night, there was the chance to work it out the next. The company usually took one programme with them. This generally consisted of a full-length work such as *Swan Lake* or *The Sleeping Beauty* to open with, a triple bill, and then another three or two-act ballet to close the week. This would be repeated up and down the country, and Wall recalls a certain amount of monotony unless he experimented with and developed roles he was given. As has already been mentioned, John Field was an invaluable mentor, helping him to develop his stagecraft and an interest in wider aspects of theatre. At the same time, Erling Sunde, a Norwegian who had danced with Western Ballet Theatre had been brought in to teach the touring company, and he and Wall formed a great *rapport*. 'The dancer I am', he said in 1974, 'is part from what I learned in class with Erling Sunde, and what I learned as a performer from John Field.'

Wall's first leading role was the boy in Kenneth MacMillan's Edwardian hothouse of a ballet, *The Invitation*, in which youth is corrupted by experience. This had already been seen at Covent Garden, with Christopher Gable in the part. Gable had left the Touring Company for the Resident at the time Wall had joined, and he seemed destined to take over the position of company 'star'.

Ashton's romantic *The Two Pigeons* had also been danced by Gable, partnering Lynn Seymour, and these two dancers taught the roles to David Wall and Alfreda Thorogood. It tells the story of an artist in turn of the century Paris who leaves his betrothed in order to follow a gypsy girl to her encampment, where she betrays him. He is attacked and robbed before returning to the girl who loves and forgives him. The inclusion of two real pigeons who are also reunited in the final scene adds to the immense charm of the ballet. David and Alfreda had danced together as a Fairy and her Cavalier in the prologue of *The Sleeping Beauty*, but this was the real beginning of their partnership. Together their emotional and stylistic rapport thrilled the audience, and it was followed by other works like MacMillan's *Concerto* and, much later, his *Mayerling*, in which Thorogood's Mary Vetsera, the besotted girl who formed a suicide pact with Prince Rudolf of Bavaria, remains unforgettable. Her passion, waywardness and sexuality were matched by perfectly controlled dancing and impeccable technique. With David's unequalled interpretation of Rudolf, their partnership reached a peak, the only lengthening shadow being their impending departure from the company.

Alfreda left first, preceding David to the Royal Academy of Dancing where she took the Professional Dance Teachers course. She is now Deputy Ballet Principal of the Bush Davies School. The Royal Ballet never exploited her potential, although she had a loyal following in the regular audiences, and it was personally painful for both her and David to see her continually passed over so that she was working hard to maintain her technique for just a few leading performances a season. It had been very different in the days when they were members of the Touring Company under John Field, but in 1970 the two companies amalgamated as the Royal Ballet, and both David and Alfreda joined the Covent Garden company as principals.

They had married in 1967, living first in one room in a friend's house in Fulham, then moving to their own house in south-west London. They have a daughter, Annaliese, born in 1972, and Daniel in 1975, by which time Frederick Ashton had retired as Director of the Royal Ballet, and Kenneth MacMillan had been appointed, at first as joint Director with John Field who soon left to become ballet-master at Teatro alla Scala, and then with Peter Wright as Associate Director.

Wall was a perfect MacMillan dancer, responding to the dramatic demands with insight and intelligence. He once said that his whole career evolved alongside actors, and there are many among his personal friends. His Romeo was full of youthful ardour, and having seen and admired in productions of the play, Ian Holm, John Hurt and Tom Courtenay, and been much impressed by the Zeffirelli film (which he describes as a 'landmark') he found his own interpretation evolved naturally. His first Juliet was Lynn Seymour, on whom the role had been created and he was influenced to some extent by her feelings, but from the outset knew they were on the same 'wavelength'. His admiration of MacMillan's choreography was absolute. 'You could do it with your head in a paper bag and people would still get the feel of it.'

He continued to develop the role, finding fresh inspiration from the Russian conductor Ahronovitch who came over to conduct a number of performances at the Royal Opera House, and who, as Wall described it, put 'fresh breath into the production' because of his understanding of Prokoviev's score. Hard work was alleviated for him by the music, particularly in the narrative ballets. With the third act of *Mayerling*, leading to the double shooting of Mary and Crown Prince Rudolf, it was Liszt, he says, that got him through. Sometimes, when he walked on with the equivalent of a marathon ahead of him, he didn't quite know how he would get to the end, with all the stops out, technically and dramatically.

In *Romeo and Juliet* he also brought his acting talents to Mercutio, bringing out the fun and charm and wit of the character. In *Manon*, MacMillan's full length work based on the Prevost novel, he danced the humorous role of Lescaut, the amoral brother of Manon who he encourages to forsake love for material possessions. The drunken *pas de deux* in the brothel in Act II demonstrated his ability to make audiences laugh, never turning character into caricature. He was also cast in this ballet as Des Grieux, the student who falls in love with the bewitching but faithless Manon Lescaut and gives up everything to follow

Above right *As Crown Prince Rudolf in* Mayerling, *David Wall created the longest and most demanding role ever written for a male dancer. Here he is partnering Merle Park.*
Right *David Wall and Lynn Seymour as the young lovers in Frederick Ashton's* The Two Pigeons. *These two dancers both possessed a powerful dramatic presence which reached its peak in Kenneth MacMillan's ballet* Mayerling.

her when she is deported to Louisiana, where she dies. Wall found it stimulating and valuable to dance Lescaut when Anthony Dowell was Des Grieux, then Des Grieux when Dowell was Lescaut. It was the same when they alternated Romeo and Mercutio. Both knew what was needed. 'I loved to be on stage' said the altruistic David Wall, 'as part of somebody else's performance.' He was always a company man, not a star with an ego concerned only with his own performance and his personal effect on the audience. When teaching his roles to other dancers, he is equally generous, as, he insists, others have always been to him. Coaching Wayne Eagling and Stephen Jefferies for *Mayerling*, he did not try to influence their individual interpretations, but to pass on 'what Kenneth had given to me'. Later, after he had retired from the Royal Ballet, he came back to teach Anthony Dowson the role, working on the 'emphasis and phrasing and musicality' as a basis for a personal insight into the character of the desperate Prince Rudolf.

It follows naturally that partnering was something he enjoyed, working with a ballerina, communicating through movement. He thinks the aptitude came through his early professional years with the touring company, when, owing to a shortage of male principals, he would be partnering two or three different girls each week. There was no time for artistic temperament, it was a matter of perfecting a sure technique. In classics like *Giselle, Coppelia* and *Swan Lake* he partnered most of the company ballerinas and in the autumn of 1966, at the age of 20, he was promoted to principal, and partnered Margot Fonteyn in *Swan Lake*. It was a performance to which he brought added dramatic dimensions. He was the youngest Siegfried ever in the company, the youngest partner she had had—she was old enough to be his mother—and although he was terrified at the prospect, he remembers the experience as friendly and helpful.

He was continually adding to his range of roles; Oberon in Ashton's *The Dream;* the dual part of Drosslmeyer and the Prince in Nureyev's *The Nutcracker;* the Golden Hours variation in MacMillan's show-stopping ragtime *Elite Syncopations.* In Glen Tetley's *Voluntaries* and Jerome Robbins's *Dances at a Gathering* he demonstrated his range as an artist—technically brilliant, emotionally moving, always a perfect team member.

In 1977 he received the *Evening Standard* Award for the 'Most Outstanding Achievement in Dance'. For a year beset with injuries to male principals, he had virtually sustained the company and given outstanding performances in three new works. The other contender was Mikhail Baryshnikov, but the judging panel decided that the marvellous work of David Wall throughout the year was more meritorious than the meteoric appearance of the Russian star.

He accepted his award after a performance of *Mayerling*, the role of Prince

D·A·V·I·D W·A·L·L

Rudolf being the longest and most demanding ever created for a male dancer. The programme by London Weekend Television on the creation of the work which showed Wall both in rehearsal and performance, *MacMillan's Mayerling*, subsequently won the *Prix Italia*. Injury to a knee which had previously given trouble, prevented him from performing the American première of the ballet in Los Angeles. It was a bitter disappointment, and there were more to follow. Although there were six more years to come before his decision to leave the Royal Ballet and other roles with which to make his mark (most notably in two MacMillan works, *Gloria* and *Isadora*), he became increasingly unhappy with the company management. He felt there were injustices, presumably mainly to do with casting, and he knew that he could not tolerate continual confrontation or, on the other hand, remain silent about a situation he believed to be wrong. With typical common sense he decided he had no wish to become old and bitter in the company. He had achieved a great deal in his career, and he was still young enough to develop in other ways.

On Wednesday, 24 October 1984, he chose *Mayerling* for a special farewell performance at the end of his twenty-first season with the Royal Ballet. The Opera House was packed. There were many curtain-calls and the stage was strewn with flowers thrown from the auditorium. Kleenex were in evidence backstage as well as front of house. The General Director of The Royal Opera House, Sir John Tooley, included a personal farewell in the printed programme that night, and it serves to sum up the achievements of a still-young man embarking on a fresh aspect of his career.

For more than 20 years David Wall has played a leading part in the life of the Royal Ballet Companies. He has demonstrated a rare combination of outstanding personal achievement and consistent commitment to the Company ideal, and his performances in a wide range of roles will long be remembered.

We are sad to be saying goodbye to David tonight, but we wish him well in his new career at the Royal Academy of Dancing, and thank him for the great pleasure he has given as a performer and for the part he has played in the development of The Royal Ballet.

His words were echoed by dancers and spectators alike.

L·Y·N·N S·E·Y·M·O·U·R

The ballet that is indelibly associated with Lynn Seymour is Kenneth Macmillan's version of *Romeo and Juliet*, premièred in 1965, although she had already made her mark in two previous MacMillan ballets, *The Burrow*, and *The Invitation*. MacMillan, in fact, is the creative figure that bestrides her dancing career, providing her greatest triumphs as well as, in at least two episodes, some sad and bitter moments.

Seymour was born Berta Lynn Springbett in Wainwright, Alberta, Canada, on 8 March 1939. Most of her childhood, however, was spent in Victoria, Vancouver Island, where she, her elder brother Bruce and her mother had moved early in the Second World War in order to be near her father who was stationed there in the army.

At six Seymour took tap lessons; later she enrolled in the Rosemary Deveson Dance Studios where she began studying ballet which, more and more, she found to be a refuge from 'humdrum domestic life'. She also secretly hoped that her growing prowess as a dancer would equate, in her father's eyes, with her brother's strong athletic ability. There may have been sibling rivalry but Seymour has always loved and admired her brother.

A visit to a matinée of *Coppelia* by the Ballet Russe de Monte Carlo and the film *The Red Shoes* compounded her growing commitment to the art. Her teachers were Jean Jepson and Nicholas Svetlanoff, a Russian emigré who implanted in Seymour her first awareness that ballet was not only graceful but also dramatically expressive.

In November 1953 the Sadler's Wells Ballet (now the Royal Ballet) visited Vancouver and held auditions. Seymour attended, performing for the ballet-mistress, Ailne Phillips, and under the alert eye of Frederick Ashton. Later that day a telephone call informed her she had been accepted as a scholarship student to the Sadler's Wells Ballet School in the autumn of the following year—the only successful applicant auditioned by the company on that tour.

Leaving her family and her homeland to live in cold, bleak digs in London was a tremendous emotional wrench for Seymour and throughout her days at the Sadler's Wells School she felt very alone, very much an outsider. She attributed this to her Canadian background although, at that time, there were several students from the British Commonwealth in the school. But it was a feeling that never left her and doubtless contributed to a 'longing to belong' that appears to have been a dominant emotion throughout her career. It is significant that her greatest

Lynn Seymour as the young Anastasia in the second act of Kenneth MacMillan's full-length version of Anastasia.

rapport at the Sadler's Wells School was with Brazilian-born Marcia Haydée who was later to become prima ballerina with John Cranko's Stuttgart Ballet and another dancer with exceptional dramatic gifts.

Lonely, homesick, unable to 'fit in', Seymour lived only for her dancing and treasured the few words of praise—'very *nice* Springbett!'—from her revered ballet teacher Winifred Edwards, and the even more rare remark from Dame Ninette de Valois, Founder-Director of the company and the school. Distant as de Valois may have seemed, she had, in fact, noted the special qualities Seymour possessed and had long-term plans for nurturing her career.

At the end of her training Seymour was not placed in either of the Royal Ballet companies but in the Covent Garden opera ballet, the traditional resort of the least promising of the students. Some months later she joined the Royal Ballet Touring Company (now called the Sadler's Wells Royal Ballet) and after spending several weeks in the *corps de ballet* de Valois advised MacMillan, who was producing a new ballet for the company, to 'have a look at the young Canadian dancer Springbett', adding 'we'll have to do something about that name!'

MacMillan looked. He was immediately attracted by Seymour's soft, expressive style and her dramatic presence on stage and cast her as one of the young lovers in his harshly realistic ballet *The Burrow*, involving a group of characters hiding in an attic from oppressive State Police—a theme similar to, but not based on, *The Diary of Anne Frank*. Seymour instantly attracted attention in her allotted role and thus began a long association with MacMillan who, over the years, created for her a succession of wonderful parts. It was for the première of *The Burrow* that Seymour changed her name, arrived at after a lively discussion with MacMillan and the group of dancers and friends that had formed a small coterie around him.

Soon after the first performance of *The Burrow* the company undertook an eight-month tour of Australia and New Zealand. During that time de Valois' plans for Seymour became evident: she made her début in the technically demanding dual role of Odette-Odile in *Swan Lake* in Melbourne on her nineteenth birthday. Although there were a number of technical faults in the performance the quality of her dancing impressed the critics as well as a number of distinguished and knowledgeable people who saw her, including Sir Robert Helpmann who had coached her in the role. He was also instrumental in Seymour changing her off-stage image, from the rather dowdy blouses, skirts and 'sensible' shoes she affected to clothes that flattered her figure, frivolous hats and high heels.

A year later Seymour made her début in *Swan Lake* at Covent Garden and the London critics agreed that here was a new ballerina possessed of unique qualities.

The following season she consolidated her position as a rising star with a performance in the title role of the Romantic classic *Giselle*. That same season she also appeared in MacMillan's *Le Baiser de la fée* (The Fairy's Kiss), danced to the Stravinsky score with a scenario based on Hans Anderson's story about a fairy who saves a baby from death and then returns, 20 years later, to claim him on his wedding-eve. Seymour was cast as the bereft fiancée and, once again, the exquisite quality of her dancing and the warmth of her on-stage personality was remarked upon by the critics.

But it was MacMillan's next ballet, *The Invitation*, which finally established Seymour as a dancer of unrivalled dramatic talent. The ballet's scenario featured an erotic quadrille in which the awakening sexuality of two adolescent cousins is affected by an embittered married couple. The boy is seduced by the older woman, the girl brutally raped by the husband. The ballet achieved some notoriety because of its subject matter (it was 1960, still a few years before the advent of the 'permissive society') but it also confirmed MacMillan as the most interesting and innovative of Britain's young choreographers, and Seymour's performance as the young girl whose innocent flirtation with the older man leads to a tragic climax was simply sensational.

It was not just the expressiveness of her dancing that was so affecting but also the power and range of her histrionic ability; the transformation from adolescent girl to physically and psychologically damaged victim facing frigid spinsterdom as a result of her experience was deeply moving. London audiences witnessed the emergence of a truly great dancer and MacMillan had found his muse.

Christopher Gable had played the part of the young male cousin seduced by the older woman and also won enthusiastic reviews for his performance. Their work together began a long, firm friendship and a short but brilliant stage partnership. Gable was one of the friends who could not help contrasting Seymour's poise and authority as an artist with her ingenuousness and vulnerability as a private person.

Seymour's next triumph was in considerable contrast to that of *The Invitation*. From the stark realism of that ballet she was cast as the young girl in Frederick Ashton's lyrically romantic *The Two Pigeons*, a reworking of a sentimental nineteenth-century work by Louis Merante to music by Andre Messager.

Through an intervention by Fate, when the dancer cast for the male lead fell ill, Seymour was once more partnered by Gable. Their youth and charm were just right for the roles of the young Parisian artist who deserts his girlfriend-model for a glamorous gypsy, gets mauled by her male companions and returns, contrite, to his true love.

Throughout the next three years Seymour appeared with both Royal Ballet companies, performing a large number of roles in the regular repertories, adding constantly to her reputation as an artist of great dramatic range and sensibility. It was during this period that she became a close friend of Colin Jones, also a dancer with the company who was planning to leave the ballet and become a photographer. His quiet, sensitive, humorous disposition appealed to Seymour and there was considerable emotional rapport between them. They were married in Vancouver in 1963 when Seymour was on tour with the main Royal Ballet company and Jones, who had begun his new career, was on an American assignment.

That same year MacMillan choreographed a fragment of Prokoviev's great score for *Romeo and Juliet*—the balcony scene *pas de deux*—for Canadian TV, using Seymour and Gable as the star-crossed lovers. Later that year, when Ashton, who had taken over from de Valois as Director of the Royal Ballet, commissioned MacMillan to create the full-length work, he naturally built the eponymous roles around the talents of the two young dancers who complemented each other so beautifully on stage.

Work progressed smoothly, with long exploratory talks between MacMillan and his chosen dancers, and then—Seymour found she was pregnant. Her agonizing choice was between having the child and starring in what she knew would be a major work in the company repertoire, between motherhood and what would be the peak of her career. For someone so dedicated to her art the decision was foregone . . .

While Seymour had an abortion in a London clinic, with all the physical and emotional trauma such an operation entails, her husband was on a photographic assignment in Leningrad. When he returned there was an estrangement between them that marked the beginning of the end of their marriage.

Another trauma was about to occur: not long before the première of *Romeo and Juliet* it was announced that Margot Fonteyn and Rudolf Nureyev would be dancing the first performance. The decision had been made at the insistence of Sol Hurok, the impresario who would be presenting the Royal Ballet in New York some weeks later; he wanted to sell the company on the strength of the two superstars in a brand-new full-length work. Their London debut would, of course, excite the interest of American balletomanes.

Both Seymour and Gable accepted the bitter disappointment—they had naturally looked on the work as *their* ballet, given that they had been so totally involved in the working out of the leading characters—with good grace, although it was a cruel blow. But for Seymour there was worse to come: when the cast lists were announced she was down as the *fifth* cast. Remonstrations by MacMillan with the management were of no avail; Ashton was the Director of the company and that was that. As it happened, owing to the illness of one of the dancers, Seymour did give the second performance, partnered by Gable. The interpretation was considered by most critics to surpass all others, the very epitome of Shakespeare's young lovers portrayed by dancers whose partnership had reached a thrilling maturity. But the incident convinced Seymour that the Royal Ballet management did not really value her talents.

Soon after the success of *Romeo and Juliet*—and it was one of the greatest triumphs ever seen at Covent Garden, with a record 43 curtain-calls—Seymour left her husband. The gulf that had opened between them was unbridgeable. She continued dancing with the Royal Ballet until 1967, and then came a major change of direction.

MacMillan was offered the Directorship of the Berlin Opera Ballet which, after some hesitation, he accepted. He invited Seymour to accompany him as his prima ballerina and, knowing how he valued her dancing and that he would be creating new roles for her, she readily agreed. MacMillan also took with him another Royal Ballet principal, Vergie Derman, as well as Ashley Lawrence as his Musical Director.

Accommodation was found for the British contingent in a vast Berlin apartment by Ray Barra, MacMillan's ballet-master recruited from the Stuttgart Ballet, where they all lived for some time as a happy little community working on a repertoire that was to establish the Berlin company as an important force in German ballet.

Seymour's time in Berlin was, however, a fairly dramatic one, both on and off stage. MacMillan created several works for her, including the beautiful abstract *Concerto* (now in the repertories of some five other companies world-wide) and a one-act Expressionist ballet, *Anastasia*, based on the claim of Anna Andersen to be the Grand Duchess Anastasia, sole survivor of the Russian royal family murdered by the Bolsheviks. Seymour's blazingly dramatic performance in the title role received wide acclaim and the ballet appealed very much to the Berlin audience's preference for dramatic works. Before the first night Seymour contracted a blood clot in her arm and was in hospital for some weeks, but recovered in time to dance on the first night.

When the Berlin season ended for the summer Seymour flew to New York to discuss making a film about a dancer with the director Herbert Ross, to be written by Terence Rattigan. At their brief meeting Seymour disliked Rattigan, thought the story very phony and the project came to nothing.

During the following winter Seymour danced the role of Aurora in MacMillan's sumptuous production of *The Sleeping Beauty*, designed by the late Barry Kay. MacMillan also mounted his ballet *Las Hermanas*, based on the Lorca play *The House of Bernarda Alba*, first produced for the Stuttgart Ballet, in which she scored another notable success.

At this time both Seymour and MacMillan had moved out of the Berlin apartment. Seymour was having an affair with a dancer in the company, Eike Waltz, half-German, half-Polish, with whom she embarked on a deliberate plan to have a baby. The plan worked even more successfully than she anticipated: Seymour gave birth to twin boys, Jerszy and Adrian.

After the birth of the twins Seymour returned to the Berlin company and danced there until the expiration of MacMillan's contract in 1969. (At the beginning of his period in Berlin he had been offered the Directorship of the Royal Ballet in 1970 when Ashton was due to retire.) Her last major role in Berlin was as Odette-Odile in MacMillan's much-admired production of *Swan Lake* designed by Nicholas Georgiadis.

After Berlin Seymour spent 18 months in an artistic limbo, a dancer without a company, dancing wherever and whenever she could—as a guest star in Barcelona with Rudolf Nureyev, with Roland Petit's company which was touring in Canada, in one performance of *The Sleeping Beauty* with the London Festival Ballet, partnered by Peter Martins (star of New York City Ballet and now its Associate Director). During this 'gypsy life' the twins spent most of their time with their father in Berlin. Seymour's own feelings of depression at the separation enforced by her nomadic life were buoyed up by her friendship with Nureyev.

In 1970 MacMillan took up his position as Director of the Royal Ballet and soon invited Seymour to rejoin the company and star in his new, expanded version of *Anastasia* which he planned as a full-length ballet. For various reasons *Anastasia* had to be postponed and Seymour's first reappearance with the company was in Jerome Robbins's beautiful suite of dances, *Dances at a Gathering*, to piano music by Chopin.

Delighted to belong to a company again and the feeling of security it brought, Seymour raised the money for a mortgage and bought a house in Chiswick, west London, near to the Royal Ballet rehearsal studios. It was the first proper home of her own and brought a sense of permanence and stability to her life. She appeared in Glen Tetley's avante-garde *Laborintus*, in the full-length classics *Giselle* and *Swan Lake* and in *Anastasia* when it was given its première in 1971. The ballet was coolly received by the critics but Seymour was much praised for her brilliant realization of the title role.

Left *Lynn Seymour as Anna Andersen, the woman who claimed to be Anastasia, sole survivor of the Russian royal family. The one-act expressionist ballet* Anastasia *also serves as the third act of Kenneth MacMillan's full-length version.*

Right *Lynn Seymour as Natalia Petrovna in Frederick Ashton's* A Month in the Country, *first produced for the Royal Ballet at Covent Garden in 1976.*

Those first three years back with the Royal Ballet were, in terms of her performances, golden years for Seymour—and her audiences. She was at the height of her powers, technically proficient and with her histrionic powers virtually unmatched by any other British ballerina, particularly in those roles created for her by MacMillan. Her special expressive qualities too, glowed with an equal effulgence in the classical and neo-classical works (such as *Les Sylphides* and *Apollo*) in which she appeared.

Off-stage she was not so happy. Her appearances with the Royal Ballet, although rapturously received, were comparatively few (at that time the company possessed 11 other ballerinas as well as *prima ballerina assoluta* Margot Fonteyn, who was still dancing). As a result Seymour fell victim to depression; she put on weight and some scheduled appearances were cancelled which made her more depressed—it was a vicious circle. She went into a slimming clinic and while there a visiting friend brought along a companion, Philip Pace, a young photographer whose humorous, rebellious temperament she found appealing. When Seymour left the clinic Pace moved into her home with her. The house usually had a succession of visiting friends and dancers, as well as a nanny for the twins and the domestic scene was more often than not rather chaotic.

When Seymour became pregnant again she decided to marry Pace. Seven months later she gave birth to another boy, Demian. At Covent Garden MacMillan decided to revive *Anastasia* and asked Seymour to recreate the title role. At 36 she made a remarkable 'come-back', dancing with all her old strength and power and receiving a tremendous ovation for a surpassingly brilliant and moving performance.

Looking slim and svelte and appearing with great success in several of her old roles, as well as new ones, her career was once again in top gear. Unfortunately, the long hours in class, in rehearsal and performance began to upset her relationship with Pace who resented the intrusion of her profession into their private lives. As well as her busy schedule with the Royal Ballet, Seymour also agreed to dance with Robert North at a gala given by London Contemporary Dance Theatre.

The Royal Ballet went on tour to Greece and Pace was further incensed that Seymour was away from London. Their growing separateness and animosity came to a head during rehearsals for a refurbished *Romeo and Juliet*. Returning from a night on the town they had a blistering row and Seymour fled from the house to nearby friends. In the morning Pace had gone.

The next three years were a kind of apotheosis of Seymour's career as a dancer—brilliant in the classics, in ballets by Ashton, MacMillan and Tudor, beloved by audiences and critics, her private life with the three boys ordered and happy.

Seymour began an affair with Robert North, principal dancer and choreographer, at that time, with London Contemporary Dance Theatre, who encouraged her first attempts at choreography, which proved successful. Then her dancing received a set-back when gynaecological trouble demanded surgery. Recovering, she made another memorable return to Covent Garden in the title role of MacMillan's *Manon*—albeit for only one performance, on New Year's Day, 1976, and followed that a month later with another great personal triumph, creating the role of Natalia Petrovna in Ashton's *A Month in the Country*. Soon afterwards she began early rehearsals for MacMillan's next full-length work, *Mayerling*, scheduled for February 1978.

In the interim she guested with Nureyev in his seasons at the London Coliseum, and with American Ballet Theatre in New York, dancing in *Swan Lake* and Tudor's *Pillar of Fire*. Back in Britain she portrayed Carabosse (a mime role) in de Valois's new production of *The Sleeping Beauty* and then, partnered by Nureyev, gave three memorably beautiful performances of Aurora in that ballet.

That same year Seymour choreographed her first major ballet, *Rashomon*, for Sadler's Wells Royal Ballet. The theme was that of the famous film by Akira Kurosawa in which a bandit attacks a newly-married couple in a forest; the tale is told from the personal point of view of each of the three protagonists. The ballet provided three strongly dramatic roles (with Robert North as guest artist in the part of the bandit) and the work was a popular success.

In 1977 Seymour's affair with North was concluded and MacMillan decided to resign as Director of the Royal Ballet in order to concentrate on choreography. He was replaced by Norman Morrice who had been a dancer and choreographer with Ballet Rambert, as well as its Associate Director. According to Seymour, Morrice did not respond to her plea to be used as much as possible during her last few years as a ballerina, and, indeed, her appearances with the company were rare.

Her last great success with the Royal Ballet was in creating the role of Mary Vetsera in MacMillan's *Mayerling*. As the social-climbing young mistress of Crown-Prince Rudolf of Austria-Hungary, danced by David Wall, her performance was, once again, sensational. MacMillan created a succession of amazing *pas de deux* for Rudolf and the women in his life, particularly for Vetsera, physically abandoned, emotionally charged, acrobatically inventive, leading to the final tragic climax of the double suicide at the royal hunting lodge at Mayerling. The ballet, its principals and large supporting cast received great acclaim, both in

London and on tour in America soon after the première. It was also featured on LWT TV, winning the prestigious Prix d'Italia prize in the music section.

In October of that year, 1978, Seymour created her second ballet for Sadler's Wells Royal Ballet, *Intimate Letters*, a romantic story using Janacek's second quartet as the chosen music. Seymour commissioned Gillian Freeman (who had written the scenario for *Mayerling*) to write the scenario, but Seymour's conception, which also included a taped collage of voices, was somewhat over-elaborate for a one-act work which also placed the musicians on stage with the dancers, to suggest a musical salon. Nevertheless the ballet had many merits and provided a strong central role for Galina Samsova.

Some weeks before the première of *Intimate Letters* Seymour had been approached by the Intendant of the Munich Opera House with the suggestion that she should become the Director (Ballettdirectorin) of the Bavarian State Ballet. Seymour saw it as a challenge and accepted—despite advice that the theatre was riddled with factions, jealousies, intrigues and restrictive practises.

At the time her contract as a dancer with the Royal Ballet still had some time to run so that, initially, she was shuttling back and forth between London and Munich.

The reports of treachery and intrigue in Munich proved all too true. From the first Seymour met, at best, obstruction; at worst she was faced with every snide trick it was possible to devise, from members of the company and theatre staff to local critics. Her two years there were a wretched, fraught experience, with every effort she made to mould the company into one of some significance sabotaged.

Seymour's Munich contract was responsible for another unhappy episode. Around the time that she decided to accept the Munich offer, MacMillan told her that he would be using the life story of Isadora Duncan as the basis of his new full-length ballet. It was a subject he had considered ever since he had read an article about her during his period in Berlin. But the resources available to him there were inadequate to his conception; now he proposed to create the work in time for the fiftieth anniversary of the Royal Ballet. Naturally, Seymour was the ideal casting for the role of Isadora (she had already danced some small solos devised as a gala piece by Ashton 'in the manner of Isadora Duncan') but MacMillan found it impossible to choreograph such a complex work around Seymour's talents if she were absent in Munich. Reluctantly, he had to cast another ballerina in the part. From the many roles made for her by MacMillan, both in the Royal Ballet and in Berlin, Seymour knew how closely he liked to work with his prima ballerina in developing a part, and yet she found it difficult to understand why he should replace her in the central role of Isadora. Both artists, MacMillan and Seymour, have differing stories to tell about why she did not create the role of Isadora; for an outsider it is easy to see that, between the emotionally volatile, wayward dancer and the hypersensitive, introspective choreographer, there was a sad lack of communication.

When Seymour's contract with Munich was 'amicably and mercifully terminated' in 1980, she returned to London. The Royal Ballet blandly indicated that they did not want her back. A sprained ankle seemed the last straw in a catalogue of major and minor misfortunes and in a mood of desperation she booked herself into the haven of a private clinic which affected some rest and emotional restoration.

The Royal Ballet rehired Seymour to dance in *A Month in the Country*, *Romeo and Juliet* and *Manon*—a repertoire that might have been designed for her. Her first performance was scheduled for 29 January 1981. Slogging away in class each day seemed more and more of an effort; doubts about her ability to maintain the standards of her previous performances nagged at her mind.

At a gala for single-parent families Seymour elected to dance a solo specially choreographed by William Forsythe, a bizarre piece about a mad housewife. Amongst the more familiar gala fare it seemed an error of judgement. Once again Seymour felt an outsider amidst the ballet establishment. Trudging home from class one cold January afternoon Seymour realized she did not want to dance any more. The Royal Ballet released her from her contract.

For the next year or so Seymour drifted happily, feeling free, taking up various projects, some of which came to fruition, some of which did not. Early in 1983 she married again, Vanya Hackel, a man of mixed Irish and Russian descent, a producer in show business. They bought a large house in Hampshire and for a time life seemed happy and settled. The marriage lasted for a couple of years and then broke up.

In recent years Seymour has freelanced as a choreographer and teacher around the world, with considerable success. In the summer of 1987 Ballet Rambert (now Rambert Dance Company, directed by Richard Alston) premièred a new work by Seymour, *Wolfi*. As the title suggests it was a typically irreverent look at the life of Mozart, danced to the composer's Piano Concerto No 21 popularized by the film *Elvira Madigan* and designed in a high-camp manner by Andrew Logan. The ballet was generally dismissed by the critics as being too frivolous for such subject matter.

In the autumn of 1987 Seymour appeared on stage again in the character role of the mother of the painter L. S. Lowry in Gillian Lynne's ballet *A Simple*

Man, created for Northern Dance Theatre based in Manchester. The part of Lowry was danced by Christopher Gable who was appointed Director of the company about the same time. It was a happy reunion for both artists, acclaimed by the press for their strongly characterized, sensitive performances. It seems a good augury for the future and no doubt there are moments when Seymour, once more back on stage, can hear the voice of her beloved teacher, Winifred Edwards, saying 'Very *nice*, Springbett!'

Like two other great Danish dancers of the twentieth century, Erik Bruhn and Peter Schaufuss, Peter Martins left the confines of the Royal Danish Ballet to extend his art. The restrictions, of course, were not due to political repression which prompted the defecting Russians to leave their companies for the same reason. The Royal Danish Ballet, concentrating on maintaining its magnificent heritage of works by August Bournonville, offers comparatively little in the way of modern repertoire. It does, however, include George Balanchine's *Apollo*, and it was this work which changed Peter Martins's career and life.

He had danced the title role in Copenhagen only weeks before Balanchine was searching Europe for someone to replace the injured Jacques d'Amboise at the Edinburgh Festival. Martins turned out to be the only available dancer who knew the work, the last choice. He had been taught by Henning Kronstam, who created the role in Denmark and was director of the Royal Danish Ballet, but after the first performance in Edinburgh, Balanchine changed every detail. It was the difference, Martins felt, between being taught the role by an interpreter and being taught by the choreographer. Balanchine's continuing creativity with a work already claimed as a masterpiece fascinated Martins, who was already considering offers from Stuttgart Ballet, London Festival Ballet and the National Ballet of Canada. The week in Edinburgh decided him. Balanchine, he said, gave him a 'fix'. He continued to guest with New York City Ballet until he joined it permanently in 1970.

Peter Martins did not choose to become a dancer. His father was a civil engineer, but his mother came from a theatrical family and she made the decision for her son, who entered the Royal Danish Ballet School at the age of eight. She made the same decision for her two daughters, but they were not accepted. Martins is inclined to believe that his sisters' rejection and a certain amount of antipathy he suffered himself was due to his uncle's collaboration with the occupying Germans during the war. This uncle, Lief Ornberg, a principal dancer with the Royal Danish Ballet, was a brilliant dancer, so handsome and blond that one distinguished Danish critic described him as 'Heavens answer to Hitler's Ayrian prayers'. He was the answer to Hitler's prayers in more ways than one, recruiting Nazi sympathizers and denouncing fellow citizens. His wife, a soloist* with the company, later became a critic on a Nazi paper, and although society took its revenge by jailing them both after the war, the family were still held in some disapprobation, even, perhaps, the nephew who was not born until 1946.

The exact date was 27 October, and when he was two his parents were divorced.

---

* In Denmark the highest rank is soloist, equivalent to principal elsewhere.

P·E·T·E·R M·A·R·T·I·N·S

Mother and three children moved to a small flat and apparently his training began early with social dances for which he showed considerable flair. Once he was accepted by the Royal Danish Ballet School he travelled daily from home across the city by bicycle or bus, beginning the day with ballet classes, academic subjects being covered in the afternoon. The basis of the ballet curriculum was the Bournonville style with its accent on elevation and fast footwork. His first teacher was Erik Bruhn and then, after a month or two, Stanley Williams, who proved to be inspirational. (Martins, in fact, does not recall the lessons from Bruhn, although he was his idol throughout the 10 years' training.)

Williams stressed precision and turn-out, classical correctness and style, not extravagant virtuosity, teaching in a way that was not exactly Bournonville, which was rather frowned upon by the authorities. He had immense respect from his pupils, and in return, he greatly respected them and their burgeoning talent. Martins worked hardest in Williams' classes, but his relationship with other teachers was not so harmonious. There was one point when he was threatened with dismissal and only the intervention by Williams saved him.

The curriculum included music theory and piano which gave Martins understanding and appreciation, although as an adult he admits he can neither play nor read a score. From 14 to 17 he was taught partnering by Frank Schaufuss, dancer, choreographer and ballet-master—father of Peter Schaufuss, present director of London Festival Ballet. Unlike his fellow students, Martins preferred partnering to dancing a solo, never thinking of it as taking second place to the ballerina but as an essential half of the choreographic whole. He puts this down partly to his lifelong love of women, feeling no need to promote the macho male image asserting a dominant personality.

There is no doubt that, like all pupils of the school, Peter Martins made his first stage appearance in the last act of Bournonville's *Napoli*, when children from the school crowd on to the scenic bridge to watch the dancers perform an endless series of brilliant tarantellas which bring this popular classic to a close. In 1964 he graduated, entered the company as an apprentice member, and married Lisa La Cour whom he partnered in *Moods*, choreographed by Hans Brenaa, to music by Franz Liszt. The following year he became a full member of the company and danced principal roles in Bournonville's *Konservatoriet*, *Napoli* and *The Kermesse at Bruges*. He was also in Birgit Cullberg's

Peter Martins as Apollo, the role in which he originally came to the notice of Balanchine. He had danced it with his own parent company, the Royal Danish Ballet, before replacing the injured Jacques d'Amboise with the New York City Ballet visiting the Edinburgh Festival.

Moon Reindeer and was performing it the night his son was born. Nilas was named after the ballet's hero—perhaps it is as well that Martins wasn't dancing in *Giselle* or *The Sleeping Beauty*—and, for the record, followed his father into the Royal Danish Ballet School.

It was not long before Peter Martins began to receive invitations to guest abroad, none of which the company management allowed him to accept. In 1966 he added *The Nutcracker* to his repertoire, and danced in Balanchine's vivacious *Symphony in C*. In 1967, the year he danced *Apollo* and made his cataclysmic visit to the Edinburgh Festival, he was promoted to soloist. It was one of those extraordinary coincidences that the night he received the somewhat desperate approach from New York City Ballet, he was dining with his old teacher, Stanley Williams, currently guest teacher with that company. During the main course, Martins began to question Williams about it and the possibility of joining. During the dessert the telephone rang with the ballet grapevine at work. Vera Volkova, the internationally famous Russian teacher who was then Artistic Advisor to the Royal Danish Ballet, told Martins that the ballet-master of New York City Ballet, John Taras, was in the Copenhagen theatre waiting to audition him. At first Martins refused. It was, after all, 11 p.m. But he succumbed and the following morning both he and Williams were on the plane.

Peter Martins's highly successful partnership with Suzanne Farrell in *Apollo* in Edinburgh led to an invitation to dance with her again, this time in Balanchine's version of *The Nutcracker* during the Christmas season in New York. The new year took him back again for the Balanchine *Swan Lake, Liebeslieder Waltzer, Symphony in C* which he had danced in Denmark, and the *Diamonds* section of *Jewels*, Balanchine's full evening work to different composers: *Emeralds* to Fauré, *Rubies* to Stravinsky and *Diamonds* to Tchaikovsky. In 1969 he once more divided his time between Denmark and America, the country that had fired his imagination even before his association with New York City Ballet. When he had asked Stanley Williams about the company, it was with America foremost in his mind. He believed that only in the United States would he be fully challenged, fully stimulated. His dream was that of many ambitious young men in other professions and other places, ever since the tide of immigration began. He loved Denmark but it was too small and too limiting. He could count the ballet dancers, he was already a soloist. What was there left to follow?

That year Martins danced in *Ballet Imperial*, Balanchine's beautiful tribute to his classical heritage, performed to Tchaikovsky's Second Piano Concerto, first performed in 1941 and in the repertoires of many companies. (The New York City Ballet version was renamed *Piano Concerto No 2* in 1973.) He also partnered Suzanne Farrell in Jerome Robbins's *Dances at a Gathering*, the first work that Martins did for Robbins, giving him an intimation that they were not in professional harmony. Years later he was to reflect: 'I feel my way of dancing never appealed to Robbins', although roles were created on him in *In the Night*, *Goldberg Variations* and *In G Major*, and he danced in other major Robbins works.

It was 'Mr B' who had inspired Martins, and he joined New York City Ballet as a principal just as Suzanne Farrell, who had married and fallen out with Balanchine, left to join Bejart's Ballet of the twentieth century in Brussels. This event was disconcerting for Martins because their acclaimed and personally satisfying partnership had been one of his chief reasons for finally leaving the Royal Danish Ballet. The move to America also ended his own marriage.

He took a bachelor apartment in the 1960s, near Central Park, designed on several levels which included a sunken living room. It all seemed very American and he was ready to start his new life. His hopes were high but they were disappointed as he tried to establish his place within the tightly knit company with its inevitable internal rivalries. He had, too, to adapt his Bournonville training to Balanchine's equally stylized, highly personal development of Petipa's brilliant classical vocabulary. Some Balanchine works he found extraordinarily close to Bournonville ballets, but he learned that for a Stravinsky piece Balanchine expected very different dancing than for, say, the Bizet *Symphony in C*. In Denmark a dancer was the dancer he was; with Balanchine a dancer had to be many kinds of dancer and perform in whatever style he required. 'When Balanchine puts you in certain ballets, he expected you to be those ballets.' In Denmark once a role was given to a dancer, it remained his role until he retired. In New York if Mr B didn't like the way it was done, he simply gave it to someone else. 'My vanity was upset.'

Martins was working with Robbins again on *In the Night* to Chopin nocturnes, his pendant work to the greatly praised *Dances at a Gathering*. Possibly his feeling out of sympathy with the choreographic method contributed to Martins's increasing disillusionment. He partnered Violette Verdy on the première of the ballet on 29 January 1970, and although his performance was well received it did not change his growing feeling that by joining NYCB he had made the wrong move. Consequently he began negotiations with American Ballet Theatre, and arrangements were almost completed when he decided to confront Balanchine and make an attempt to sort out the difficulties. Whatever passed between them, the conclusion was that Martins stayed with New York City Ballet for the rest of his dancing career.

The Stravinsky Festival in 1972 was a turning point, with four new Balanchine

Right *Peter Martins in George Balanchine's* Violin Concerto, *to the work by Igor Stravinsky. Martins was one of the original cast when the ballet was premièred in 1972.*

Left *Peter Martins in Balanchine's brash, ebullient* Stars and Stripes. *Martins' brilliant technique, virile presence, and good looks made him one of New York City Ballet's most popular male dancers.*

ballets all premièred in June. In particular *Violin Concerto* and *Duo Concertante*—
in both of which Martins partnered Kay Mazzo—provided a happy and successful
relationship with Balanchine. In *Symphony in E Flat* he partnered Gelsey
Kirkland, the emotionally disturbed ballerina with whom he was later to have
a brief relationship when his long-term affair with another dancer, Heather Watts,
seemed to be coming to an end. In Kirkland's 'tell-all' autobiography she records
that the two of them planned to leave New York City Ballet and find works in
which they could dance together. If he had serious intentions, Kirkland's transfer
of affection to the newly arrived Baryshnikov, and the return of Suzanne Farrell
to the company put an end to dreams of 'defection'.

For a dancer whose technique and training made him an outstandingly noble
premier danseur in classical roles such as Prince Florimund in *The Sleeping
Beauty*, it is interesting to speculate on the direction his career would have taken
had he in fact joined American Ballet Theatre with its wide-ranging repertoire.
As it was, Peter Martins's combination of film-star good looks, fine dancing and
strong stage presence made him a star in a company which, officially, does not
promote stars. His stellar rise through the seventies can be traced by the roles
he took and created in Balanchine works. Between 1974 amd 1982 he danced
in *Agon*, one of the most difficult, innovative, rhythmically taut ballets the
choreographer ever created; his version of *Coppelia*, in which Martins was a
sunny, open Franz; the evocative *Afternoon of a Faun*; *Tzigane*, created with
Suzanne Farrell, and the raucous razzmatazz entitled *Stars and Stripes*. Among
other ballets in the Balanchine repertoire were the lush *Vienna Waltzes*, which
Martins created with Kay Mazzo as his partner; *Orpheus*, yet another work to
a Stravinsky score which he first performed during the annual summer season
at Saratoga in 1979, and *Mozartiana*, again partnering Suzanne Farrell, his
last role in Balanchine's lifetime.

During this same period, Martins was, of course, very much at ease in
Bournonville Divertissements staged for New York City Ballet by Stanley Williams.
There were, too, important Robbins ballets; *Other Dances* and *The Four Seasons*
in which he followed Baryshnikov, and *Fancy Free* which Martins said 'killed
me . . . murdered me, absolutely'. The story of three sailors on leave (the basis
for the musical and film, *On the Town*) which Robbins choreographed to music
by Leonard Bernstein, greatly appealed to Martins. 'When I was called for *Fancy
Free* I was ecstatic.'

Once again working with Robbins proved to be a miserable experience. Martins
ached for the freedom to add his own small character touches, but Robbins
refused to allow even the slightest innovation. Instead of being liberated by the

all-American role he felt he really understood and which embodied the fun and freedom of his adopted country, Martins was depressed and trapped.

In 1970 he guested with the National Ballet of Canada and with London Festival Ballet, where he partnered Maina Gielgud in *Swan Lake* and Lynn Seymour in *The Sleeping Beauty*. Seymour and Martins found an immediate rapport on and off stage, having a brief affair at a time when both artists needed emotional support. A decade later Martins told Seymour that he had been influenced by her devil-may-care approach to dance, lessening the psychological pressures that were bedevilling his life.

In 1977 he danced an excerpt from Balanchine's showpiece *Tchaikovsky Pas de Deux* with Suzanne Farrell in Herbert Ross's film with a New York ballet setting, *The Turning Point*. The same year he choreographed *Calcium Light Night*, his first major ballet, one of several he has continued to produce for New York City Ballet which include *Lille Suite* in 1980 and the suite from Stravinsky's *The Soldier's Tale* in 1981. Balanchine's influence is apparent in all these works and it would be fair to say that Martins has yet to find his own choreographic style, but his output serves to provide a flow of new works each season which has always been an essential part of NYCB's appeal.

In 1981 he was made ballet-master of the company. Two years later George Balanchine was taken seriously ill and died on 30 April 1983. Jerome Robbins and Peter Martins were together appointed Ballet Masters in Chief, a somewhat curious title that means, in effect, that they are co-directors. Their aim is to keep the Balanchine repertoire and style alive. This they have done, reviving works, maintaining standards of the irreplaceable Mr B. Of his own future, Peter Martins has said, 'I have no idea what my contribution will be . . . I'm not talking historically—I don't care about that. I care that I can inject a lot of life and energy and knowledge and thought into the next generation.' He spoke with the altruism that is common to all great dancers as, in their turn, they pass on the works and the techniques and the tricks and, above all, the passion to those who, for a few decades, are guardians of their art.

S·U·Z·A·N·N·E F·A·R·R·E·L·L

George Balanchine, Diaghilev's last and greatest choreographer, finally settled in the USA where he founded the School of American Ballet and American Ballet, from which the New York City Ballet evolved. After a number of early works with narrative themes such as *Apollo*, *Prodigal Son* and *Night Shadow* Balanchine concentrated more and more on plotless ballets, selecting a variety of scores from Mozart to Tchaikovsky, Hindemith to Stravinsky, upon which he based his neo-classical abstract choreography.

He took the basic classical steps and presented them in a new way, frequently off-balance, inverted, distorted, turned-in instead of turned-out. This distinctive style produced a new type of dancer, the Balanchine dancer, fast, athletic, developing great stamina, ready to experiment, for which the young dancers of America were both physically and temperamentally ideal.

Balanchine's personal love of women plus, in the early years, the great preponderance of female students and dancers, produced a line of devoted acolytes ready to place themselves at 'Mr B's' disposal. Pre-eminent among these, the archetypal example of a Balanchine dancer, is Suzanne Farrell.

Born Roberta Sue Ficker on 16 August 1945, in Cincinnati, Ohio, she was the youngest of three sisters: Donna, the eldest, studied ballet; Beverly, the middle sister, studied the piano, and Sue, from the age of eight, accompanied her eldest sister to ballet class. Their mother, a divorcée, resumed her maiden name of Holly and worked as a nurse, specializing in the care of terminally ill patients, to support her daughters.

Sue Holly's once-a-week ballet class also included acrobatics which, initially, held more appeal for the little girl — 'I was very supple and liked doing daring, even dangerous, things, backbends, cartwheels, flips and so on.' When the Ballet Russe de Monte Carlo (the last remnants of what had been Diaghilev's company) came to Cincinnati, Sue was chosen to dance the role of Clara in *The Nutcracker* with Cuban-born Alicia Alonso and Russian-born Igor Youskevitch as the principals. Later, at the age of 12, 'there was a moment' when the somewhat sterile appeal of acrobatics was suddenly superseded by the expressive power of ballet: rehearsing with her class for a lecture-demonstration of Michel Fokine's *Les Sylphides*, Sue stood on the empty stage of the Cincinnati Music Hall looking out into the dark auditorium and 'knew I was a dancer — that I had to dance.' As a small, private token of that revelation she knelt and picked up a splinter from the stage to commemorate the moment. She still keeps that sliver of wood in recognition of the moment when she was professionally dedicated to the Goddess of the dance, Terspichore. In actual fact she is a dedicated Roman Catholic, and as well as fancifully serving some mythical Goddess in the pantheon

of the arts she firmly believes 'I dance for God, who gave me the gift of dancing'.

From that revelatory moment in the dark, musty Music Hall, Sue spent every available minute in ballet class. She began listening to as much music as possible, which was freely available in the Cincinnati Conservatory of Music where she studied, she spent hours in the library reading about ballet and looking at pictures of ballerinas from earlier periods. She organized a fan club for the New York City Ballet, the company which most attracted her, and made up dances for the members of the club to perform.

Yet, instead of finding role-models in the ballerinas of the day the young adolescent dancer found inspiration in an image of the Virgin Mary in her Catholic school and, later, in the story of the young St Joan of Arc whose struggle against malevolent forces was an encouragement in moments of doubt or failure.

With her sisters Sue's favourite game was 'Ballet': Donna was the teacher, Beverly the mother and Sue the 'promising pupil'. It was a game which they all took very seriously. They also put on shows at home for friends and neighbours, revues, dancing, baton-twirling, acrobatics, with Sue creating dances to popular songs like *Just One of Those Things* and *I Cover the Waterfront*.

In many of these home performances, given with her best friend in Mrs Holly's front parlour, Sue imagined herself partnered by one of the leading dancers of New York City Ballet, Jacques d'Amboise, but it is significant that, in these fantasy moments, she always retained her own identity, never imagined herself as any New York City Ballet ballerina.

At the Conservatory Sue's teacher was Nelle Fisher who was also Ballet Director for the summer opera season staged (of all organizations!) by the Cincinnati Zoo. Sue took part in performances of *Aida*, *Carmen*, *Salome* and *Macbeth*, which provided valuable stage experience.

When the New York City Ballet came to Bloomington, Indiana, Mrs Holly took the girls to see a programme that included Balanchine's *Symphony in C*, a large company display-piece to the symphony by Bizet. In the theatre Sue was transfixed by this piece with its endless cascade of brilliant classical steps, and at home she tried to recapture some of its sections in a solo performance. This intense experience and its domestic aftermath convinced Mrs Holly of the necessity of moving to New York city to secure the best available training for her daughters although, while she knew that her specialized nursing would always provide her with employment in the metropolis, whether she could make enough

Suzanne Farrell was frequently partnered by Peter Martins. This photograph, taken during a performance of Balanchine's Allegro Brillante, *illustrates the exultant style of her dancing.*

for them to live on as well as paying for the girls to have first-class instruction was doubtful.

Happily, after auditioning in front of one of New York City Ballet's senior dancers, Diana Adams, Sue Holly obtained one of the few scholarships available for the School of American Ballet, thus alleviating Mrs Holly's financial burden. Although Adams thought that Sue had bad feet she felt it was a flaw that could be overcome by proper training. Sue's other attributes, a high extension, a soft, lyrical way of moving, were sufficient recommendation to take her as a pupil. We can also assume that the astute Adams also discerned that the anxious little girl also possessed an absolute dedication to her art.

Mother hen and her three chicks arrived in New York city on a hot summer day in 1960, their worldly possessions piled into a rented car and trailer. The possessions included a grand piano (presumably it travelled in the trailer) which imposed some difficulty in choosing accommodation: the family could only afford one room but that room had to accommodate them all as well as the huge musical instrument—landlords were somewhat alarmed to see what was going to be packed into the apartment. Initial accommodation was found in the Ansonia Hotel on Broadway and 73rd Street. Waiting outside with the goods and chattels Sue had to reassure passers-by that she was not a waif who had been evicted on to the sidewalk!

Almost the first thing that Sue did was to Gallicize her first name into Suzanne and choose a new surname—one with a better theatrical sound—from the telephone book. Suzanne Farrell was born.

If the quarters she shared at the Ansonia with her mother and sisters was cramped (it was not long before Donna married and went to live upstate) Sue did not mind: her real 'home' was the School of American Ballet where she arrived early each day and left late in the evening. On Sundays she attended mass and prayed that she would be worthy of the hopes her family and teachers held for her. Those hopes were very soon realized. That first Christmas Farrell was recruited to be an Angel in Balanchine's production of *The Nutcracker* for the New York City Ballet. Then, a mere year after entering the school, she was taken into the company. She was only 16, the youngest member of the New York City Ballet and, while still in the *corps de ballet*, she was given a leading role in Balanchine's beautiful *Serenade*, his first work created in America and a ballet that had become a signature work for the company. Then Diana Adams fell ill and Farrell took over her role in another major ballet, *Concerto Barocco*, created on Bach's Double Violin Concerto. It was a measure of her technical capability that she should have been chosen for these two important works.

1963 proved another year of considerable achievement. John Taras chose Farrell for the leading role in his new ballet *Arcade*, danced to Stravinsky's Concerto for Piano and Wind Instruments. Her partner was Arthur Mitchell (the first black dancer to join the company who was to go on and found the Dance Theater of Harlem) whose virility, technical virtuosity and sheer joy in dancing was splendidly complementary to Farrell's feminine grace and lyricism. Both dancers performed in a wide range of the repertoire, particularly in the Balanchine works—the demanding, innovative *Agon*, the austere *Metastaseis*, the jazzy *Slaughter on Tenth Avenue*.

Farrell was given a number of partners whose masculine presence accentuated her seeming fragility, although there was also a steely strength in her dancing. Among her partners was—yes! Jacques d'Amboise, the dancer about whom she had fantasized in her mother's front room; he, in particular, seemed to provide a kind of insouciance that was a splendid foil for her serious demeanour. If there was a criticism to be made about her dancing at that time it was that there was too much reserve, not enough projection, of an on-stage personality. That, of course, was a factor resulting from Balanchine's idiomatic choreography: many of his dancers tended to seem like dancing machines rather than flesh and blood artists.

One of Balanchine's more austere works was *Movements for Piano and Orchestra*, to another score by Stravinsky. This was a second half of an earlier work, *Monumentum Pro Gesualdo*, which had been created three years before. This second part was created on Farrell and d'Amboise and both dancers achieved personal successes with their roles at the ballet's première on 9 April 1963. Farrell was not yet 18.

In those early years Farrell not only danced in a large part of the NYCB repertoire but many roles were created on her, including Balanchine's complete recreation of *Don Quixote*. Premièred on 28 May 1965, with a score by Nicholas Nabokov, it was one of Balanchine's rare full-length works, a spectacular production which included live animals, elaborate costumes and special stage effects with, of course, the inevitable windmills. Balanchine himself played the part of the Don, fantasizing about his ideal woman, Dulcinea, danced by Farrell as the recurring figure of Servitude, Fidelity, Romance and Youth. It was a tremendous burden for a young dancer to carry but, although Farrell had not yet developed anything that could be called a stage personality, her very youth and gaucheness seemed right for the role which must project innocence and purity. At any rate it catapulted her into the limelight and she instantly became one of the most talked-about Balanchine ballerinas.

Farrell's next created role was in Balanchine's *Brahms-Schoenberg Quartet*, another of the choreographer's large-scale plotless works, this time based, as the title implies, on Schoenberg's lush scoring of Brahm's Quartet No 1 in G minor. There were many bravura solos in the piece and the finale was done in a flamboyant Hungarian gypsy style. Farrell's co-dancers included such established NYCB stars as Melissa Hayden, Allegra Kent, Patricia McBride, Edward Vilella and Jacques d'Amboise. Within three years of joining the company Farrell had joined the front rank.

Almost exactly a year later Balanchine devised another full-length work, only this time, instead of being based on a well-known classic tale it was an evening-long plotless work, the first such ballet in any repertoire. It was inspired by a conversation with Claude Arpels of the famous New York jewellers Van Cleef and Arpels. The three movements represented three rare jewels, Emeralds, Rubies and Diamonds, for which Balanchine used three disparate scores: a section of Gabriel Fauré's *Pélléas et Mélisande*; Igor Stravinsky's Capriccio for Piano and Orchestra, and the slow movement from Tchaikovsky's Third Symphony. Farrell and d'Amboise danced the leads in the last section, Diamonds, and if both the score and choreography seemed rather flowingly lyrical to represent something as hard and glittering as diamonds, then it did not matter with either audiences or critics for the ballet received great acclaim. So did Farrell; partnered once more by the man about whom she had fantasized as an adolescent, they both achieved a personal triumph in the work, entitled simply, *Jewels*.

One year on and Farrell was engaged in another Balanchine première, *Metastaseis and Pithoprakta*, which received its first night on 18 January 1968. About as far removed from the neo-classicism of *Jewels* as it was possible to get, it represented Balanchine's brief flirtation with the electronic scores which were currently fashionable: the music was by Iannis Xenakis. The first section was a very unballetic sequence that seemed to represent elemental creatures emerging from primeval ooze. In the second section Farrell and Arthur Mitchell performed together as two Adam and Eve characters, supported by the primitive figures from the first section. It was not a popular ballet, just a necessary nod in the direction of what came to be called 'modernism', a stylistic movement as transient as art nouveau, art deco, cubism and fauvism. From the dancers'

Above right *Suzanne Farrell was the perfect example of a Balanchine ballerina, combining feminine grace with a steely technique. Here she is partnered by Arthur Mitchell in Balanchine's difficult, innovative* Agon *to the score by Stravinsky.*
Right *Suzanne Farrell was not only capable of great technical virtuosity but also possessed expressive elegance, a quality revealed in this photograph taken during Balanchine's* Vienna Waltzes.

point of view it was useful only as an excursion into contorting their bodies into a new plasticity.

By this time it is fair to say that Farrell had become Mr B's favourite ballerina, the dancer he first thought of when creating a new ballet, forged over a number of years as the perfect and very willing instrument upon which he could plan his kinetic experiments. During the last three years or so only two ballets and some *pas de deux* were created for other dancers. Balanchine's preference for Farrell had become almost an obsession.

Some 12 years previously Balanchine's fourth wife, the beautiful, witty French-born Tanaquil Leclerq, had tragically contracted poliomyelitis during a tour of Denmark and had been confined to a wheelchair. During that time Balanchine had been a solicitous husband-nurse, attentive to all his wife's needs. Now, in 1969, his obsession with Farrell as a dancer spilled over into his private life. Having made generous financial settlements on Leclerq, he hurried to Mexico for a divorce; back in New York he proposed marriage to Farrell. He was 69, she was 24 and already in love with a handsome young dancer in the company, Paul Meija. Balanchine was contracted to arrange the dances in a production of Glinka's *Ruslan and Ludmilla* in Hamburg; he left New York in a mood of black despair, vowing never to return. He did, of course, due in great part to the persuasive good sense of his long-serving devoted secretary Barbara Horgan.

The situation was untenable (although, when Balanchine had married Leclerq, his previous wife, Maria Tallchief, had remained as a principal dancer with the company; no doubt Balanchine could cope with the conflicting egos of ex-wife and current wife as ballerinas in his company: what he could not cope with was another male as part of the triangle). Suzanne Farrell and Paul Meija were married while Balanchine was in Germany. They then resigned from the NYCB.

After her resignation Farrell made only one brief appearance in New York, in a short ballet choreographed by Meija to the second movement of Mahler's first symphony, as part of a musical evening given at the Brandels High School in Manhattan. Farrell was then invited to dance as a guest artist with the National Ballet of Canada; during a performance of *Swan Lake* she sustained a serious knee injury which, for a time, seemed to indicate the necessity for an operation. After a long rest, however, the knee healed naturally.

During that period Farrell was approached by Maurice Béjart with an offer to join his company, the Ballet of the Twentieth Century, based in Brussels. Béjart went to New York to talk to Farrell, then invited her and her husband to Montreal to see the company where it was on tour. Farrell accepted Béjart's offer and he also engaged Meija, both as dancer and choreographer.

Farrell and her husband arrived in Brussels, together with their three cats, in November, 1969. She gave her first performance with the company that December, in Béjart's *Sonata*. Other roles which subsequently followed were in *Erotica*, *Messe Pour le Temps*, *Mathilde*, *Vier Letzte Leider* and Juliet in Béjart's version of *Romeo and Juliet*. Farrell was well aware that Béjart's choreography for women was very 'thin'—his large contingent of men invariably receiving much the most interesting work. Béjart, however, knew that he had one of Balanchine's greatest dancers as a principal and made roles specially for her.

One of these special roles was as Laura in *The Triumph of Petrarch*, based on the life of the great lyric poet of the Italian Rennaissance and his unrequited love for Laura, the wife of a nobleman. Even so, the ballet—like so many of Béjart's works—was successful as spectacle rather than dance, the choreographic content being both minimal and banal. In this work she established, as far as the text allowed, a rewarding partnership with one of Béjart's most splendid male dancers, the Argentinian-born Jorge Donn.

There was a certain irony in Farrell's return to New York in February of the following year: the dance-goers and balletomanes of that city attended the performances of the Ballet of the Twentieth Century not so much to see Béjart's ballets as to welcome back their renegade ballerina. Farrell appeared in another Béjart spectacular, *Nijinsky: Clown of God*. In this supposed ballet-biography of Nijinsky (Diaghilev was depicted by a giant, malevolent figure, manipulating Nijinsky's career and life like a pupper-master) Farrell played the duel role of goddess of the dance and guileful woman—presumably Romola de Pulsky, Nijinsky's wife. As with the Petrarch ballet, the role was banal and unrewarding and there were those in New York who were either sad or gleeful to see Balanchine's great dancer so under-used.

Farrell's work with Balanchine had divided the regular ballet-going public into two distinct camps: those who were uncritically adulatory and those who were dismissive of almost all she did, saying that her dancing was too cold and mechanical, facile, over-elaborate. The break with Balanchine had, of course, fed the gossip columnists with a rich vein of rumours and, in a magazine interview, Farrell said 'so many writers have distorted our statements and misquoted our exact words to the extent that we feel we have been persecuted and lied about in the press'.

Farrell and her husband remained with Béjart for nearly five years. In retrospective interviews she has been discreet and loyal in her references to Béjart although she must have been aware that it was hardly the ideal company to display her talents. Yet while with the Belgian company she and her husband did a daily Balanchine *barre*—Meija made a tape of music that Balanchine had used—and Farrell practised several of her Balanchine roles: 'My body needed it and I needed it spiritually', she said.

Farrell returned to the NYCB in the summer of 1974. She went to Saratoga in upstate New York (where the company have a regular summer season) and watched the company in performance. She sent Balanchine a note, saying 'As wonderful as it is to watch your ballets, it is more wonderful to dance them. Is this impossible?' It was an obvious proffering of the olive branch. Balanchine sent for her: 'We met, and the topic of discussion was "when do we get back to work?" Nothing more.' Commonsense prevailed; Mr B realized he needed one of his best, most dedicated dancers and Farrell realized that the NYCB was her natural home. But Balanchine refused to accept Meija back into the company; instead, he joined Maria Tallchief, Balanchine's third wife, as co-Director of the Chicago City Ballet from which he was dismissed, suddenly, in 1987. Farrell and Meija are still married. There are no children.

The first work in which Farrell reappeared with NYCB was in the adagio, the third movement of *Symphony in C*, in New York on 16 January 1975. On that occasion she was suffering from a high fever, sore throat and nervous anxiety in case she should not be able to do justice to Balanchine's work. She had no need to worry: the New York fans applauded her as soon as she stepped on to the stage; she was given four curtain-calls when the movement was over and a solo call after the ballet.

While she had been dancing with Béjart, Farrell had missed the much acclaimed Stravinsky Festival by the NYCB in 1972—her only expressed regret in leaving the company. In the year in which she rejoined she was able to take part in the Ravel Festival, for which Balanchine created *Tzigane*. It began with a five minute solo for Farrell, utilizing all her gifts as a dancer; it was a star turn, framing her special ability at off-centre poses and with her steely classicism and exploiting the greater ability at projection which was the legacy of her period with Béjart. It re-established her as a leading principal with the company: without words Balanchine was saying 'all is forgiven'.

Throughout the next few years—during which the School of American Ballet, founded by Balanchine and Lincoln Kirstein, one of the chief creative forces in American ballet—celebrated its forty-fifth year, Farrell continued to dance the many roles that she had acquired before joining Béjart. She also acquired a new partner, Peter Martins. This tall, handsome young man had first danced with the NYCB company during a season at the Edinburgh Festival in 1969, when he was called in from his 'home' company, the Royal Danish Ballet, to replace an injured dancer in *Apollo*. Martins' first two years with NYCB had been extremely difficult, Balanchine humiliated him in class, mocking his 'beautiful' classical style; Martins weathered this period, painfully discovered the style that Balanchine wanted and became the company's *premier danseur noble*. After Mr B's death in 1983 Peter Martins became Associate Director of the company with Jerome Robbins.

During the Ravel Festival Farrell, with Martins as her partner, created the leading role in *Concerto in G*, a plotless work by Robbins. Something of a pendant to his *Dances at a Gathering*, was *Other Dances*, also premièred by Farrell and Martins. In 1977 came *Bournonville Divertissements*, staged by the British-born, Danish-trained dancer and teacher Stanley Williams, a dance suite based on choreography by the great nineteenth-century choreographer August Bournonville.

In June, 1977, Balanchine conceived what was to be his last really large-scale work—and, albeit somewhat schmaltzy—one of his most successful: *Vienna Waltzes*. Using music by Johann Strauss (*Tales from the Vienna Woods*), Lehar (the waltz from *The Merry Widow*) and Richard Strauss (*Rosenkavalier*), it was conceived as an evocation of Vienna in its final post-Romantic hey-day, girls in swirling ballgowns, men in dazzling Hussar uniforms or formal evening wear. Farrell introduced the last sequence of dances from *Rosenkavalier*, dressed in a ballgown with a long train, sparkling with diamonds, performing an interrupted solo broken by the intrusions of a shadowy partner, her lover, danced by Peter Martins. It was a role in which she appeared with a new personality, no longer the sharp, fast, crystal clear epitome of the athletic Balanchine style but something more mysterious, more palpably flesh and blood: a fascinating, mature woman. *Vienna Waltzes* was a smash-hit with the general public, even if some critics thought it a shallow crowd-pleasing work; it stayed in the repertoire for four seasons and every performance was sold out.

Not long after *Vienna Waltzes* Farrell began to suffer from the onset of a troublesome hip, culminating in two hip replacement operations during the eighties. She has borne this tragic situation with typical fortitude, sustained by her unwavering Catholic faith. Her intention is, following the success of the operations, to rejoin the company but, at the time of writing, this has not happened. Now in her early forties, it would seem unlikely.

Farrell has been a total product of the Balanchine system, the perfect specimen of the ideal instrument for his style, a role-model for all dancers of a younger generation who saw her. Whether she will pursue a career teaching and coaching dancers in the parts she made famous it is impossible to foresee, perhaps presumptuous to suggest. But she will be remembered as a great dancer.

nthony Dowell has been, to date, the greatest *premier danseur noble* trained and produced by the Royal Ballet system. There has been a long line of distinguished male dancers in the company since its inception in 1931—including Anton Dolin, Robert Helpmann, Harold Turner, Michael Somes, David Blair, Christopher Gable. Only Donald MacLeary, however, can be said to have rivalled Dowell as the perfect classical prince, combining a perfect line with technical virtuosity and stage presence, but right from the beginning of his career Dowell has been pre-eminent in such roles, not just within the ranks of the Royal Ballet but also when measured against international stars. Moreover, the roles created for him by Frederick Ashton, Kenneth MacMillan, Antony Tudor, Hans van Manen and Glen Tetley have provided a range of parts, an opportunity for dramatic expression, not even surpassed by Rudolf Nureyev.

Comparisons, however, are not only invidious but also pointless. All great dancers bring their individual, inimitable qualities to the roles they dance so let it just be said that Dowell has been richly endowed with all the necessary attributes of the *premier danseur.*

Dowell has said that he enjoyed an exceptionally happy childhood. His father was in shipping and his mother loved dancing and the home life and atmosphere was serene and loving. 'I always thought . . . that everyone had a happy time with their parents, that all parents acted towards each other as mine did.' This childhood idyll was shattered some years later when both his parents died young, first his mother and then his father. His later adolescent years were spent with two aunts.

Doubtless influenced by their mother's love of dancing, both Dowell and his sister went to a dancing school run by June Hampshire and both young people were taught tap, musical comedy and ballet. Dowell was 'mad about the theatre' and particularly enjoyed the annual school show given, not in a school hall, but in the Fortune Theatre, a stone's throw from the Royal Opera House. Dancing was his 'way of getting on stage', and his main childhood hobby was designing sets and costumes for his model theatre.

Dowell's sister eventually went into commercial shows and revues before marrying and leaving the theatre. Dowell's natural facility at ballet led him to go from school to the Royal Ballet School, a decision which, he says, his parents accepted without demur at a time when 'there was still a question mark about ballet as a career for a boy'. That same facility allowed him to sail through the

Anthony Dowell as Oberon in Frederick Ashton's Shakespearean ballet The Dream. *It was Dowell's first created role—and a part in which his performance has never been surpassed.*

dance curriculum with comparative ease, but he was bored by the daily academic classes and, not being a boarder, could not wait to get home to his model theatre. At the Royal Ballet Upper School he was taught by Harold Turner, a dancer who had been one of the most brilliant technicians in the early days of the company and who no doubt was delighted to teach a young man who showed a similar prowess. Dowell was also taught by Errol Addison, Margaret Graham and the redoubtable Winifred Edwards.

From the Upper School Dowell graduated into the Royal Opera Ballet which was considered the proper apprenticeship for young dancers before their appointment to the ranks of one of the two Royal Ballet companies. After a year with the Opera Ballet Dowell was drafted into the Royal Ballet at Covent Garden just as it was about to make its second visit to Russia and he was intimidated by living, perforce, in such close proximity to the principals and soloists of the company. Dowell was always shy and reserved, a quality that was evident in his stage performances for some years.

His first big 'break' came as a soloist in Erik Bruhn's production of the dances from the last act of Bournonville's *Napoli*, the fast, fleet, bouncy style in distinct contrast to the bigger, more expansive movements of the Russian school upon which the Royal Ballet style has always been based. Bruhn, at that time the greatest *premier danseur noble* outside of Russia, was very pleased to find a young British dancer who could assimilate the Bournonville style so well. Certainly Dowell's naturally pure, aristocratic manner was noticed by the critics and the regular ballet-goers at Covent Garden who were quick to spot a potential star in the making.

Two years after *Napoli*, in 1962, Frederick Ashton chose Dowell to dance the role of Oberon in his new ballet *The Dream*. In that work Dowell was matched with Antoinette Sibley, a pairing that was to initiate one of the great ballet partnerships over the next two decades or more. They complemented one another perfectly, not as temperamental opposites like Fonetyn and Nureyev, but almost as two halves of one being, a geminian couple whose pure academic style and unforced technical ease was a joy to watch.

Both Dowell and Sibley scored personal triumphs in *The Dream*—their performances as Oberon and Titania have never been matched, far less surpassed—and the ballet was reasonably well received in London, but the enthusiasm with which they and the work engendered in New York established them as the new British ballet stars and helped secure the ballet in the company's repertoire.

The following year Dowell created the role of Benvolio in Kenneth MacMillan's *Romeo and Juliet*. The work was hailed as a masterpiece and established the reputations of a number of dancers. Benvolio was a minor role but, once again, Dowell was perfectly cast, his serious mein and faultless classicism the ideal foil for the more volatile part of Mercutio. In later years Dowell was to prove one of the great Romeos, combining an inherent hauteur with youthful passion.

Two years later Dowell was chosen by Antony Tudor for his ballet *Shadowplay*. It is an enigmatic work, based partly on Kipling's *Jungle Book* and partly reflecting Tudor's own interest in Bhuddism. Tudor was one of the most exiguous choreographers, expecting not only impeccable technique but an intellectual curiosity and perceptiveness from his dancers. He never made a movement without meaning, once remarking 'I choreograph to the eyelash', and would frequently pounce on a dancer in rehearsal and ask why were they making that gesture or expression. If the dancer had no explicit reason or rational explanation he would be cruelly mocked in front of the company. The set for *Shadowplay* is dominated by a huge tree, and the ballet opens with the main character, the Boy With Matted Hair, sitting beneath it. At the first rehearsal Tudor asked Dowell what kind of tree it was; Dowell had not thought about it, just accepted it as part of the set, but he remembers that moment as the beginning of his intellectual approach to a character, a Stanislavskian technique of questioning and analysing every aspect of a performance and the environment in which it takes place.

In that same year, 1967, Dowell made his first appearance as Prince Siegfried in *Swan Lake*, guesting with the Royal Ballet Touring Company (now Sadler's Wells Royal Ballet) and the following year he was one of the cast of principals in Peter Wright's new Tennysonian-medieval version of *The Sleeping Beauty*. His beautiful classical dancing was shown to advantage in these princely roles, and he was beginning to add a youthful ardour to what are usually rather cardboard cavaliers. His partnership with Sibley was also extended when she was cast as Aurora in *The Sleeping Beauty*. These two dancers exemplified the British classical style in a ballet that had become a signature piece for the company some 20 years previously and, although the Royal Ballet policy is not to have official 'stars', British balletomanes were happy to have a new partnership of such undeniable quality and consequence.

In 1966 Dowell had also been chosen as the first cast for the role of the Messenger of Death in MacMillan's long one-act masterpiece, *The Song of the Earth*, based on Gustav Mahler's great symphonic song-cycle. It is an extremely demanding role, both technically and emotionally, and Dowell's soaring virtuosity illumined the part in a manner rarely achieved by any other dancer.

In 1967 Dowell made his début in *Giselle*, perfect casting for the aristocratic philanderer Albrecht who, in the second act, is called upon to dance a series of exhausting *pas de deux* and solo variations. He brought an emotional intensity to the first act which projected the character with great clarity, and superb classical style to the second act—although, in an interview, he admitted that the role imposed the greatest test of stamina he had, until then, had to face.

In the next few years Dowell not only danced in many ballets in the regular repertoire, including *The Nutcracker* and *Cinderella, Daphnis and Chloe* and *Symphonic Variations*, in all of which he added to his reputation as the outstanding young classical dancer in the company, but also created several important roles in new ballets. Chief amongst these were two Ashton works, his *Jazz Calender* to a pastiche jazz score by Richard Rodney Bennett and, rather more importantly, *Enigma Variations*, in which Ashton created in dance the several close friends of Elgar 'pictured within' his well-known orchestral variations of the same title. Dowell contributed a memorable bravura solo, built upon an endless series of whirlwind pirouettes, illustrating the volatile temperament of Arthur Troyte Griffith. As with so many roles created by Dowell it can fairly be said that his performances have never been surpassed by other dancers who have essayed the part.

In 1970 Kenneth MacMillan took over the Directorship of the Royal Ballet from Frederick Ashton at a time when Dowell—and his partnership with Sibley— was reaching the height of his technical powers. At that time the Board of Directors at Covent Garden had decided that the resources of the two companies should be pooled—an idea that, after a couple of years experimentation, failed to work out. The process produced a number of logistical headaches, not the least of which was that MacMillan had to find roles for no fewer than 11 ballerina principals as well as Margot Fonteyn who, although then in her early fifties, was still making a number of guest appearances. Moreover, a number of the established principals were then in the final years of their career while younger dancers of promise were beginning to expect leading roles; there was thus an awkward overlap of two generations of dancers.

The first work that MacMillan brought into the repertoire went some way to solving the problem of finding parts for a large number of soloists—Jerome Robbins's *Dances at a Gathering*, an exceptionally beautiful suite of dances for 10 leading dancers which included Anthony Dowell and Antoinette Sibley, both of whom—in a glittering assembly that included Rudolf Nureyev, Lynn Seymour and David Wall—added to their laurels with performances of sparkling virtuosity.

MacMillan's first major work of his own for the company was the one act *Anastasia*, first produced in Berlin for Lynn Seymour, developed into a full-length three-act work to show off the great strength of the company at that time.

Right Anthony Dowell as the young man in Jerome Robbins's Afternoon of a Faun, *a modern version of the Nijinsky ballet* L'Après-midi d'un Faune. *Instead of an arcadian scene it is boy-meets-girl in a dance studio.*

Left Anthony Dowell and Antoinette Sibley in Frederick Ashton's beautiful 'abstract' work Scènes de Ballet *to the score by Nijinsky.*

The extended title role was, of course, danced by Seymour but MacMillan devised a beautiful, and prodigiously difficult, *pas de deux* for Sibley and Dowell, playing the roles of Mathilde Kschessinska, prima ballerina of the Tsar's Imperial Ballet, and her partner. (Kschessinska had been Tsar Nicholas II's mistress before his marriage to Alexandra.) Dowell also danced the role of one of the three naval officers who appeared in the first act, each of whom had a bravura variation as well as dancing together.

The following year, 1972, Dowell created another leading role in a MacMillan one-act ballet *Triad*. Set to Prokoviev's First Violin Concerto, the theme of the ballet was sibling rivalry between two brothers—Dowell and Wayne Eagling— for the affections of a woman, danced by Sibley. The ballet was notable for the technical demands that the choreographer made upon all three principals, and all three achieved personal triumphs in their parts, although it was Eagling who received the greatest share of praise as he was making his first début in a major role and his character, the 'outsider' who is rejected by the other two, was the more interesting.

During the Royal Ballet's New York season in the spring of that year Dowell and Sibley both attracted the attention of the critics by virtue of their beautiful dancing together but both of them had to withdraw from the programmes because of illness and injury. But by the summer Dowell was fit enough to be chosen to partner Natalia Makarova in her début with the Royal Ballet, dancing Albrecht to her Giselle. It was significant that he had been chosen to partner this great Kirov ballerina, a reflection upon his superb classicism and the success of the occasion confirmed a second important partnership in Dowell's career: he was to partner Makarova on several further occasions when she was a guest with the Royal Ballet and, later still, when he took extended leave from the company.

1973 marked Britain's entry into the European Common Market and the occasion was celebrated at Covent Garden with a gala in which several European companies contributed. The Royal Ballet's participation, designed to show off the principal dancers, included a duet specially written by MacMillan for Dowell and Sibley, to Fauré's *Pavane*. More lyrical than brilliant, it nevertheless revealed the perfect sympathy of their partnership. In that same season Dowell made his début in the ebullient role of Colas in Ashton's *La Fille mal gardée*, something of a departure from the classical princes he usually danced, and revealing another side of his stage personality—humorous and exuberantly extrovert.

Only two weeks later, in January 1973, the Royal Ballet introduced three works by Georges Balanchine into the repertoire, and Dowell was cast in the exceptionally difficult, innovative *Agon*. An abstract work, acclaimed as one of

Balanchine's most distinctive masterpieces, its form of neo-classicism was quite alien to the British dancers but Dowell, along with the other company principals, gave a classically smooth interpretation to the angular movements that Balanchine had devised to Stravinsky's typical acerbic rhythms.

In the spring of that year MacMillan introduced a new version of *The Sleeping Beauty*. Designed by Peter Farmer the production was coolly received by the critics, but Dowell and Sibley as Prince Florimund and Princess Aurora received great praise and added further laurels to their partnership.

The autumn season of 1973 began with another work new to the repertory, Jerome Robbins's *In the Night*. Using Chopin nocturnes, the ballet was a pendant to the choreographer's *Dances at a Gathering* but on a smaller scale and more romantic in theme. Once again Dowell and Sibley scored a success as one of the three couples that made up the cast of the ballet, their lyrical classicism ideally suited to the choreography. Despite the frequent appearances of such great dancers as Margot Fonteyn, Rudolf Nureyev and Natalia Makarova that season, audiences were just as delighted by the performances given by Dowell and Sibley.

During this exceptionally busy season Dowell and Sibley had been rehearsing MacMillan's third full-length dance drama, the spectacular *Manon*, based on the eighteenth-century novel *Manon Lescaut* by the Abbé Prévost. In fact, during the rehearsal period (the ballet, from the original idea to the first night, took the best part of two years to produce) Sibley, playing the title role, had fallen ill and the major part of the choreography for the heroine was created upon Jennifer Penney who later became one of the role's greatest protagonists.

Sibley was well enough to dance on the first night in March, 1984, however, and her performance as the amoral Manon, torn between true love and the love of luxury, with Dowell as the young theological student Des Grieux, fatally obsessed by his love for her, may be considered as the apotheosis of their partnership.

Dowell was particularly suited to the role of the serious, innocent young man whose infatuation leads him to murder and degradation. At the core of MacMillan's choreography are four breathtaking *pas de deux*, each one charting the development of the relationship between the ill-fated lovers, and Dowell and Sibley performed them with the style, panache and emotional commitment that had marked the progress of their work together.

In devising Dowell's solo variations—particularly in the first act—MacMillan had made great use of the dancer's beautiful line in arabesque and his wonderfully smooth control in pirouettes, often combining the two with pirouettes into arabesque, a movement which no other dancer who has essayed the part has been able to execute with quite the same expressiveness. Fourteen years later, at the time of writing, Dowell and Sibley are still dancing these same roles together and if their techniques have not quite the same flawless perfection as in previous decades, their emotional depth and projection of character are that much greater in intensity.

At later performances of the work Dowell played the part of Lescaut, Manon's pimping, venal brother, the role originated by David Wall. Whereas Wall had imbued the part with a certain warmth, making him almost a likeable rogue, Dowell was coldly vicious, projecting the sinister qualities of the character with a power that surprised both the professional critics and his many fans. Here was undeniable evidence that the quiet, shy, elegant young dancer, so perfect for romantic heroes, had unsuspected histrionic abilities—that he could also be a most convincing villain.

In May of 1974 the Royal Ballet made another visit to New York—the first time that the company had been to America without Fonteyn as its prima ballerina—and although Nureyev was there as a guest artist it was Dowell and Sibley, making their American début in *Manon*, who garnered the most plaudits. Later in the year, during the autumn season at Covent Garden, Makarova made her début as Manon, partnered by Dowell as Des Grieux, a pairing that enhanced their reputations together, her more volatile Russian temperament revealing a greater ardour in Dowell's performance than he had hitherto displayed.

Early in 1975 Dowell appeared in a new ballet by the Dutch choreographer Hans van Manen, *Four Schumann Pieces*, the central role of which had been specially created around Dowell's talents. A plotless work danced to Schumann's A Major Quartet, its flowing lyricism with a series of swift entrances and exits for 10 dancers was accentuated by Dowell's beautifully smooth style.

Two months later Dowell created yet another role, this time in a large company display piece, *The Four Seasons*, by MacMillan. Danced to music by Verdi, the work provided bravura roles for several of the company's principals; Dowell appeared in the fast and furious Autumn section, his speed and virtuosity displayed to great advantage.

In the late spring the Royal Ballet undertook its first visit to the Far East for many years and the accent was on full-length works. After a brief stop in Korea the company spent four weeks in Japan where the dancing was much admired, especially that of Dowell and Merle Park in *The Sleeping Beauty*. Although the company has never announced a hierarchy amongst its principals—with the single exception of Fonteyn as the *prima ballerina assoluta*—there is no doubt that

Right Anthony Dowell as Des Grieux, the role he created in Kenneth MacMillan's romantic drama Manon. *The seated dancer is Jennifer Penney.*

Left Anthony Dowell as Des Grieux.

at this time most observers would have named Dowell as its leading male dancer. Certainly his following among balletomanes in London had reached the point of mass adulation; whether he was partnering Sibley, or Makarova, or Park or Seymour, he had become a real box-office attraction, programmes in which he was appearing were invariably sold out irrespective of what ballets he was dancing.

The new year of 1976 began with the last performances together of Fonteyn and Nureyev, in *Romeo and Juliet*, so that Dowell's presence was all the more important. In February he made his début in Ashton's new work *A Month in the Country*, a one-act distillation of the play by Turgenev in which a charismatic young tutor, Belaiev, disrupts the household of a mature woman, Natalia Petrovna, danced by Lynn Seymour, with his presence. Dowell charged his role with a potent mixture of mystery and sensuality with the emotional chemistry between him and Seymour providing high voltage dance-drama. With an elaborate setting of an elegant salon by Julia Trevelyan Oman, and splendid performances from a strong supporting cast, the ballet was an instant success. Yet again the role created by Dowell has never been surpassed in performance by any other dancer.

At a time when MacMillan was considering the subject of his next full-length work, which turned out to be the violently melodramatic history of the double suicide of Crown Prince Rudolf of Austria-Hungary with his young mistress Mary Vetsera, Dowell succumbed to an injury which was to prove troublesome, so much so that he was advised to take a long rest. This precluded him from creating the role of Rudolf, which MacMillan had intended and the part, perforce, was built upon David Wall who subsequently scored the greatest success of his career in the role.

In 1977 MacMillan resigned as Director of the Royal Ballet in order to concentrate on choreography and he was replaced by Norman Morrice, hitherto Associate Director of Ballet Rambert and the first person from outside the Royal Ballet to become its Director. In 1978, recovered from his injury, Dowell announced that he was leaving the Royal Ballet in order to join American Ballet Theatre.

The announcement came as a shock to his many fans but Dowell explained that he felt in need of a fresh challenge. His whole career, up until that time, had been spent in the protective womb of the Royal Ballet. Groomed for eminence from the moment he left the Royal Ballet School, he had progressed throughout the company ranks to his unarguable status as *premier danseur*. He had danced all the great classical roles as well as those of the modern repertoire, he had had splendid parts created for him, he had triumphed with Sibley as his partner as well as with other distinguished ballerinas. Now it was time to go into what he called 'experimental exile', but he sweetened the pill for those who were dismayed by his announcement by affirming that it would not be for ever.

There is no doubt that it was a wise decision. He needed new roles—even the shock of the fiercely competitive commercial world represented by American Ballet Theatre. And so it proved. His performances with American Ballet Theatre—where Makarova was his regular partner—revealed a new maturity, a new confidence after the enforced inertia of his injury, an even greater power and virtuosity in his dancing.

As it happened, one of the most important 'new' roles that he danced with ABT was not in a brand new work, but Solor in Makarova's rescension of the third act of *La Bayadère*, the Kingdom of the Shades scene, which he had already performed at Covent Garden in Nureyev's version. In his search for new horizons Dowell had gone to America where he found himself dancing a principal role in a nineteenth-century classic! Later, in 1980, Makarova produced the full length ballet in which she and Dowell both scored a notable success.

Of course, Dowell found other new roles in ABT's repertory, although many of them were, inevitably, the familiar classics—*Swan Lake, Giselle, Don Quixote*. More important than the roles themselves, however, were the opportunities to dance them far more frequently than at Covent Garden. The Royal Ballet was able to offer far fewer performances to its principals, first because the company shares the Royal Opera House with the Royal Opera, and second because the run of a given work would have far fewer performances anyway. With ABT Dowell was able, for instance, to dance six or seven consecutive performances of Prince Siegfried, thus being able to build upon the part, to relish the continuity in both technique and interpretation. With the Royal Ballet he would have perhaps only two performances of the role in a season, and those would be fairly widely spaced.

As well as his time as a permanent member of ABT Dowell also guested with the National Ballet of Canada, where the Royal Ballet principal dancer, Alexander Grant, had recently taken over the Directorship. The experience of performing to new audiences throughout the North American continent was also invaluable, a very different response to the somewhat hot-house atmosphere of Covent Garden with its regular phalanx of adoring balletomanes.

Dowell returned to the Royal Ballet in time to take part in the company's Fiftieth Anniversary celebrations in 1981, his main participation being the title role in a revival of Robert Helpmann's dance-drama *Hamlet*. It was an elegant, intense performance but, like every other dancer who has tried the part—including Nureyev—not wholly successful. Helpmann conceived it very much as a mime role suited to his own highly idiosyncratic theatrical talents at a time, 1942, when the company, because of the war, was short of virtuoso male dancers; no one has ever been able to instil the role with the same haunting incandescence.

Another Helpmann role which Dowell assumed with great style and polish was The Bridegroom in Ashton's *A Wedding Bouquet*, based upon the eccentric verses of Gertude Stein. Dowell's performance did not have the extrovert theatricality of Helpmann's but was more reserved and, many thought, all the more witty because of it.

An out and out virtuoso role, the central male lead in Ashton's *Rhapsody*, created to show off the dazzling talents of Baryshnikov, presented Dowell with a different type of challenge. He did not have the humming-bird brilliance of Baryshnikov but his own brand of classical elegance and musicality proved that the ballet was not a one-man vehicle.

Yet another Ashton work provided one of the last roles that Dowell created, the rather gigolo-like character in *Varii Capricci*, Ashton's last collaboration with composer William Walton, which had its première in New York during a brief visit by the company in April 1983 and was presented at Covent Garden in July of that year. As the title suggests, the ballet was a chic, even trivial, caprice which disappointed many people (was not Ashton entitled to have his little joke?) but it did at least bring Dowell and Sibley, who played the role of a mature woman enjoying a romantic dalliance, together again.

With Sibley's return to the stage the famous partnership was rekindled with considerable success, particularly in such ballets as *The Dream* and *Manon*. At the same time Dowell began to perform more mimetic roles, amongst which were some memorable interpretations of Carabosse, the wicked fairy, in *The Sleeping Beauty*. Reminiscent of his chilling performances as Lescaut, Dowell's conception of the character was the personification of evil, a creature of cold malevolence.

In September 1984 Dowell was appointed Assistant to Norman Morrice, Director of the Royal Ballet. In 1985 he was made Associate Director and in 1986 he took up the appointment of Director of the Royal Ballet, remarking that the undertaking prompted him to have embroidered a cap band with the words SS *Titanic*. It was a typically diffident remark from someone who had learnt, during the previous three years, just what a burden it is to administrate such a national institution. Nevertheless, within six months of the appointment he had placed his reputation on the line by producing a wholly new version of *Swan Lake*. It proved a controversial production, mainly because of the somewhat vulgar excesses of the designs, but some observers found reassurance in the quality of the dancing—particularly welcome as the company had received some fierce criticism in the preceding year or two because of undeniable evidence of falling standards of performance.

Dowell has assumed the Directorship of the Royal Ballet at a time when a new generation of young dancers are coming to prominence. It is too early to begin to assess the quality of his leadership but two things can be taken for granted: his sympathetic understanding of a dancer's needs and the wholehearted good wishes of thousands of balletomanes who remember—and still are able to appreciate—his great performances as a dancer with gratitude and affection.

Anthony Dowell was awarded a CBE in HM the Queen's Birthday Honours List of 1973, and the BBC celebrated his international status as a great classical dancer with a programme, *All the Superlatives*, in 1976.

'The world outside', Antoinette Sibley once said, 'never seems to grasp just how tough ballet is.'

She started extraordinarily young, and battled with acute homesickness, a grumbling appendix and some form of tubercular glands as well as the aches, pains and sprains of any aspiring schoolgirl ballerina.

She was six months old when war was declared in September 1939, and at 3½ years she was safely deposited at St Christopher's Preparatory School outside Shrewsbury, a haven from bombs but something of a desert for the infant heart. Her mother, Winifred, had trained as a dancer with Lea Espinosa, and thought her little daughter would be happier with the famous Cone sisters, Grace, Valerie, and Lillie, whose school was later to amalgamate with Olive Ripman's and blossom into the Arts Educational Trust. At the age of five, therefore, Antoinette was on course for a stage career, studying—alongside the general academic curriculum—musical comedy, tap, mime, acting and ballet. Ballet was the subject with the least appeal because it required the hardest work, but whether she applied herself or not, and she maintains she didn't, she passed her exams with great credit and her parents decided she should audition for the Royal Ballet School. She was nine years old and she was accepted.

All the early years at boarding school produced some likely psychological responses and even today the sight of her packed suitcase gives her 'a cold sick feeling' even if she is only going away for a weekend. Loving her family, missing home comforts, her behaviour at school was not exemplary. Wilful and stubborn her teachers said, although later it transpired that they were secretly excited by her talent and apparently Margaret Graham, one of the Royal Ballet School teachers, confided to the then grown-up Anthony Dowell that the staff knew from the start that the pair of them were outstanding and had to restrain themselves from paying too much attention to them in class. At home during the holidays she gave no indication to her parents that she wasn't happy away from them. The way she coped with depression was by putting on a carefree act, laughing and talking as if all was right in her world, her way of pretending to herself that the misery of parting was somehow not going to happen all over again.

Sibley was at school ahead of Dowell, her first teacher the seemingly formidable Winifred Edwards, a one-time member of Pavlova's company. To the child, Miss Edwards's serious approach, the discipline she imposed and the self-discipline she expected was intimidating. To the adult Antoinette Sibley, she remained

Antoinette Sibley as Titania in Frederick Ashton's ballet The Dream. *Together with Anthony Dowell as Oberon, it was this work that first established their famous partnership.*

a source of strength and her mentor, on a number of occasions coming out of retirement to help the pupil she had so often sent out of class. Her set *barre*, the particular sequence of warming-up exercises is the one that Sibley still does before
a performance, simple, strenuous, uncomplicated—the foundation of her art.

Miss Edwards was followed by Barbara Fewster, now Principal of the Royal
Ballet School, who once astonished Antoinette by praising her in class, 'You
really are a beautiful dancer', imbuing her with much needed confidence. There
was also Harold Turner, teaching *pas de deux*, and like most of the girls in the
school she was madly in love with him, wearing too much make-up and low-cut
leotards for the weekly class. There were lessons too from Peggy Van Praagh
and Pamela May, and in the senior school Errol Addison and Harjis Plucis,
then ballet-master with the company, gave her a sense of enjoyment and privilege,
each teacher in turn contributing important elements to the exceptional dancer
she was to become.

Ninette de Valois, although not teaching, was always an inspirational force,
spotting Sibley's potential early and using her to demonstrate at the summer
schools she ran for teachers who came from all over the world to learn her syllabus.
It was de Valois who, at the end of a long tour and short of dancers, took Sibley
into the company. Sadler's Wells Ballet was on the verge of becoming the Royal
Ballet, but Sibley just made it under the old name, appearing in *Swan Lake*
on 2 January 1956 as a Swan in Act II and a Page in Act III. Margot Fonteyn
was Odette/Odile, and the performance was especially memorable because she
had been made a Dame of The British Empire the day before.

In spite of being in the company Sibley was still, ostensibly, a student, and
in the first Royal Ballet School performance ever, she danced Swanilda in *Coppelia*,
and was quietly noted by the talent-spotters in the audience. Just a month or
so later, performing with the company in Croydon, she had one of those life-
changing experiences, a sense of self, a revelation. It happened late at night,
the dancers had travelled back to London and they all crowded into the stalls
circle of the Covent Garden Opera House to watch the Bolshoi's dress rehearsal
of *Romeo and Juliet*. There had been problems with the scenery and the rehearsal
hadn't started until midnight, spectators and performers all equally exhausted.
The principals, Raisa Struchkova and Alexander Lapauri, were uncertain of
something, and onto the stage, Sibley recalled, came 'this little grey-haired person
all covered in woolies', who went up onto the balcony, 'took off the woolies and
was sixteen years old'. It was Galina Ulanova. Without costume or make-up she
danced the Balcony *pas de deux*. A miracle, said Sibley, and at that moment,
as she joined in the almost hysterical applause, she understood what her own

dancing was all about. All the other ballerinas she knew were dark-haired, remote, glamorous, with qualities to which she could not aspire for emotional or physical reasons. This was a performance so real, so natural, it touched a chord. She had found a mould into which she could possibly put herself.

At this time Sibley shared a flat with several girls, none of them connected with ballet. The 'landlady' was Sheila Bloom, who has remained a close friend throughout her career and has 'helped to keep me sane in this crazy world'. Bloom described Sibley then as being scared of most things, a typically obedient and mildly neurotic ballet dancer. In fact she was finding that company life enforced all the rules of behaviour she had tried to avoid at school—going to class regularly, trying to achieve, repressing rebelliousness. Often she would look round her fellow dancers in class, serious, silent, concentrating, and squash an impulse to do something absurd.

She was rapidly being used for new roles: the Lilac Fairy Attendant, Red Riding Hood and the Fairy of the Crystal Fountain all in *The Sleeping Beauty*; Fairy Summer in *Cinderella*. On 24 September 1959, shortly after her promotion to soloist, she danced her first Odette/Odile at the Golders Green Hippodrome in north London. Ninette de Valois had given her two weeks to learn the role and Fonteyn's partner, Michael Somes, as the Prince to help her manage it in so short a space of time. The company was on tour in the provinces and Sibley had to come into London for rehearsal every morning. It was frantic and worrying, a personal Mount Everest which had to be climbed. The night arrived, she brought off the difficult Black Swan *pas de deux*, solo variations and coda with panache; gave a second performance the following week in Streatham with another partner and that was, she reasoned, her *Swan Lake*, with the company returning to Covent Garden where audiences expected to see the major ballerinas and not 20-year-old soloists. She was back to the *pas de trois*.

When Michael Somes telephoned her a month or so later to tell her she was 'on tonight' she was somewhat puzzled and said she knew. It wasn't until he rang again to say that Fonteyn had given up some of her rehearsal time to Sibley that she realized that Nadia Nerina was off and she was doing Odette/Odile at the Royal Opera House. The following year she was made a principal.

In both personal and professional terms those early *Swan Lakes* were of great significance to Antoinette Sibley. She fell in love with Michael Somes, 22 years her senior. It happened, she said, while he was partnering her, and for the next five years they lived together, on and off, until their marriage in St Peter's Church, Milden, in Suffolk, in 1964. Finding her own style within the role was a watershed in her career. The way she wanted to dance it—'very opulent, exaggerated,

Plisetskaya, back arched, legs up, crazy sort of things—did not suit her body: 'I was classical-lined.' It was Tamara Karsavina, the great classical ballerina of Diaghilev's first company, who helped her find the pure, simple line, the perfect classicism with which Sibley is associated. With the mime too, Karsavina, old and arthritic, demonstrated the role so tellingly that Sibley described the experience as 'like listening to Beethoven after just learning the scales'.

She danced her first Aurora in *The Sleeping Beauty* during the North American Royal Ballet tour in 1960, with four subsequent performances in London in the winter of 1961. It was not until 1968, however, partnered by Anthony Dowell in Peter Wright's new production, that audiences recognized her as one of the supreme exponents of the role. With scenery by Henry Bardon and costumes by Lila di Nobile, the medieval setting had its opponents, but the fans queueing for 'Antoinette and Anthony' tickets proved there were no doubts about the partnership.

They had first been cast opposite one another by Frederick Ashton when in 1964 the Royal Ballet was celebrating the quarter centenary of Shakespeare's birth with a triple bill—a revival of Helpmann's *Hamlet*, a new MacMillan work, *Images of Love*, based on various Shakespearean lines and Ashton's *The Dream*.

Ashton had decided on a Victorian version of *A Midsummer Night's Dream*, with music by Felix Mendelssohn and much consciously nineteenth-century choreography. The décor by Henry Bardon and the costumes by David Walker contributed to the period charm and atmosphere, and it is astonishing today to realize that the work, now considered a masterpiece, was dismissed as a *pièce d'occasion* by some of the leading critics. Sibley and Dowell received more commendation than the work, and there is no question that the audience responded to the harmony between the dancers as they did themselves. It was not only a matter of the perfect proportions—on *pointe* she was exactly the right height for the turns—but, as Sibley has said, of hearing the music in the same way, almost of breathing together. It is a partnership of classic perfection, and in the *Nocturne pas de deux* when Titania and Oberon are reconciled, it was seen in every aspect of its extraordinary accord, crowning the ballet, magical, sensual, loving, forgiving. Shakespeare's Immortals, through Ashton, were immortalized by Sibley and Dowell and for many ballet-goers, remain the definitive performances.

Antoinette Sibley as Princess Aurora in The Sleeping Beauty, *a role in which her beautiful classical style was shown to advantage.*

Ballet dancers are particularly susceptible to glandular fever, and three months after the opening night of *The Dream* and shortly after her marriage to Michael Somes, Sibley succumbed to it and was forced to rest from dancing. She was nursed back to health by her Royal Ballet School teacher, Winifred Edwards but it seemed from then on her career was continually blighted by minor and major injuries and illnesses. She was back with the company in 1965 to dance her created role in Ashton's Monotones 1 to music by Erik Satie which perfectly suited her cool, clear line and style, but in 1966 she was to undergo an operation on her left knee which was to continue to give trouble. The operation was followed by a nervous collapse, brought about by the strain and anxiety and possible consequences to her career.

None of this helped establish a happy marriage, but in spite of the problems it was sustained and in 1968 Sibley appeared in two new Ashton works, *Jazz Calendar* and *Enigma Variations*. In the first she danced Friday with Rudolf Nureyev (Friday's child is loving and giving), a langurous and sensual *pas de deux* to Richard Rodney Bennett's score. Designed by Derek Jarman, the ballet was tremendously popular as was *Enigma Variations* (*My Friends Pictured Within*) which followed Elgar's score of musical portraits of his wife and friends, and ended with the arrival of a telegram from the famous conductor, Hans Richter, agreeing to conduct the first performance of the work.

Sibley was the child, Dorabella, whose hesitant speech is conveyed in the music and by swift *batterie* and *changements* in the choreography. The classical variation is utterly delightful and Sibley's sweetness and charm revealed the character that so pleased Elgar and now the Covent Garden audiences. The fact that she was unwell during the rehearsal period meant that she was not able to be in the 'Nimrod' variation, the beautiful *pas de trois* for Elgar (Derek Rencher), his publisher A. J. Jaeger (Desmond Doyle) and his wife (Svetlana Beriosova), which Ashton had apparently intended as a *pas de quatre*. It would certainly have had a very different emphasis.

In 1969 the pressure of working together and Sibley's lack of experience in running a home finally broke her marriage with Somes, and they separated although they did not get divorced for several years. They were, of course, in daily contact within the company, which must have provided some stress. The company, too, was undergoing change, and in 1970 Kenneth MacMillan became Director of the Royal Ballet following Ashton's retirement. One of his first acts was to acquire Jerome Robbins's *Dances at a Gathering*, premièred the previous year by New York City Ballet. It opened at the Royal Opera House on 17 October with a starry cast including Sibley, Dowell, Seymour, Wall, Coleman and Mason and received a popular and critical ovation. It was a brilliant addition to the Royal's repertoire, and Sibley found working with Robbins an 'absolute delight'.

The following year she was to dance the London première of his *Afternoon of a Faun* with Dowell, but was given advance warning by Robbins on the night of her first Opera House *Giselle*. The summer vacation was approaching and he was afraid she would cut her hair short before relaxing in the sun and sea. He wanted it waist-length for the role. This short, atmospheric work was a resetting of Nijinsky's famous ballet from an Arcadian scene to a modern dance studio and, though slight, was a perfect vehicle for these two young artists. It was an immediate success and at the same Gala performance for the Royal Ballet Benevolent Fund, Sibley and Dowell also danced a gloriously lyrical Ashton *pas de deux* to Massenet's *Meditation* from *Thais*.

Only a month later Sibley created another new role, this time the Girl in Kenneth MacMillan's haunting *Triad*, in which two brothers (Dowell, and Wayne Eagling in his first major role) compete for her attention. There is a wonderfully erotic *pas de deux* for Dowell (the elder brother) and Sibley, while the rejected boy, callously beaten up by the Girl's companions, watches, disturbed and brooding. Sibley has commented on the very different styles of choreographing by Ashton and MacMillan; Ashton moulding the dancer, creating with her, MacMillan coming to rehearsal with most of the work already created in his head.

Ill health once again interrupted her career, this time forcing her to drop out of the company's American tour, but she added another Robbins work, *In the Night*, to her repertoire in the autumn of 1973. This was in the style of *Dances at a Gathering*, again to Chopin pieces, romantic and liked by audiences although it had only a handful of performances. This year, too, she met her second husband, Panton Corbett, at a dinner party. Like her, he had been married before, and visited her in hospital quite soon after their meeting. She had been ordered complete rest by her doctors, and all visitors were kept at bay, but he managed to find his way in with flowers, and romance followed.

This was a fulfilling time. Out of hospital and in love, she began to work on her greatest created role, Manon Lescaut, in MacMillan's full length *Manon*, based on the Abbé Prévost's eighteenth-century novel to music by Massenet (although not that from the opera) and with designs by Nicholas Georgiadis.

MacMillan had created his previous three-act ballets around the talents of Lynn Seymour, although in fact Fonteyn had danced the first performance of *Romeo and Juliet*. Subsequently Sibley was cast as Juliet, and in *Anastasia* the role of Mathilde Kchessinska was created on her. Kchessinska was a Russian prima ballerina, one-time mistress of Tsar Nicholas II father of Anastasia.

MacMillan introduced her at Anastasia's coming-out ball as part of the entertainment, and Kchessinska and her partner (Dowell) performed a brilliant *pas de deux*, dressed in elaborate black and silver costumes of the period designed by Barry Kay. It was a glittering *divertissement*, but Manon, like Juliet, was to be a fully dimensional character demanding dramatic power in equal proportion to impeccable classical dancing.

MacMillan began work on the four big *pas de deux* for the lovers which are the core of the choreography. The first one records their instant attraction for one another; the second their rapturous physical infatuation; the third the unfaithful Manon's return and the fourth her death in his arms. Only the first was completed when Sibley suffered an inflamed hip, and the rest of the role was created on Jennifer Penney.

On 7 March 1974, *Manon* received its first performance at a gala attended by the Queen Mother, and had a rapturous reception, something of a triumph for gala audiences are notorious for sitting on their hands. Almost all the reviewers gave lavish praise to Sibley, Dowell and David Wall, who danced Manon's venal brother, Lescaut. One cannot resist quoting the critic of the *Morning Star* who attacked MacMillan for his 'appalling waste of lovely Antoinette Sibley who . . . is reduced to a nasty little diamond-digger'.

Eloise, her first child was born in 1975. In 1976, while in Hollywood filming with Baryshnikov in Herbert Ross's *The Turning Point*, she sustained a massive injury to the left knee which had given her problems for 10 years. The cartilage was irreparably damaged and it was necessary to have it removed. She retired officially in 1979 and gave birth to her son, Isambard, two months prematurely in July 1980. She wanted to give time to her family, no longer feeling able to battle with physical stress. She wanted to go to the country, to read, go to the cinema and the opera, learn to drive. Ballet had been her life since she could remember, but the time had come to leave it behind.

Her friends, particularly Ashton and Dowell, thought otherwise and persuaded her to take part in the 50th Anniversary season of the Royal Ballet in 1981. Ashton devised a witty new role for her in a short ballet to a score by William Walton, *Varii Capricci*, in which Dowell played a gigolo-ish character to Sibley's elegant, mature woman. Coaxed out of retirement, she has continued to guest with the company, delighting audiences with performances in *Scènes de Ballet*, *The Dream* and *Manon*. 'Life,' she once said, contemplating her many illnesses and injuries during her best dancing years, 'is to forge ahead.' Her achievements are the testimony.

She was awarded a CBE in 1973.

'**I** love New York, as I love Moscow . . . you can work in such cities.'
The general public, aware of the defecting superstars, scarcely knows
the name of Vladimir Vasiliev who enjoys the rare privilege of remaining a Soviet
citizen while dancing freely in the West. It is ironic that if he too had 'leapt
to freedom' he would be heralded and idolized but he has chosen to fight from
within the Soviet Union, to challenge Bolshoi director, Yuri Grigorovitch's artistic
stranglehold on the company. The irony is compounded by the fact that it was
Grigorovitch's ballet, *Spartacus*, that first made Western ballet audiences aware
of this athletic and charismatic dancer called in his own country, by the renowned
dancer and choreographer Fyodor Lopukhov, 'an unprecedented phenomenon
with whom no one could be compared, including Nijinsky'.

Vladimir Victorovich Vasiliev was born in Moscow on 18 April 1940. His
father was a truck driver and his mother a factory clerk, and within the common
pattern of Soviet working-class life, young Vladimir joined the local Pioneer club,
a rather politically motivated form of Boy Scouts. There, at the age of seven
he danced in a folk troupe and found he very much enjoyed it. No one within
his family had ever been involved in the arts and it was the leader of the folk
dance company who recommended him to the Bolshoi choreographic school.
He was accepted and at the age of nine embarked on the demanding curriculum
which provided a full academic education with mathematics, literature, physics
and history of music in tandem with the rigorous dance training.

He had enjoyed folk dancing, but the classical ballet classes he was now
compelled to attend bored him. 'Dry exercises', he called them, and he often
arrived late for his class so that he missed the essential practice at the *barre*.
During those vital seven and a half years when the body is being formed, Vasiliev
sometimes skipped class altogether. It wasn't that he didn't love dancing. Character
dance, historical dance, acting and music appealed to him tremendously. He
just didn't like the classical training. Later he put it down to his lack of natural
attributes. 'I had only high elevation. I didn't have a good arch. I didn't have
a good turn-out. I didn't have a high extension.'

It was at the beginning of the final year that he had the sudden realization
that he could in fact be a classical dancer, and with this revelation he threw
himself into work, driving himself with a frenzy towards that important step in
his career, his graduation performance. In spite of his intense effort, he was
almost unnoticed. It was his partner in the *Nutcracker pas de deux* who drew
the attention with her *élan* and style and charm. Her name was Ekaterina (Katya)
Maximova and she was to become a leading Bolshoi ballerina and also his wife.

Vasiliev was taken into the Bolshoi company in 1958. His first recorded public

recognition came however at concert evening which included the youthful and fiery Rudolf Nureyev in the *Le Corsaire pas de deux*. Vasiliev played the jealous villain, Gianciotto in Alexei Chichinadze's *Francesca da Rimini* and made great impact with the sinister character role. Galina Ulanova, prima ballerina of the Bolshoi, was astute enough to recognize his classical talent, and chose him to partner her in one of her last performances of *Chopiniana* (retitled *Les Sylphides* by Diaghilev but retained in its original form by the Bolshoi). It was not suited to his appearance or technique, and later he was to comment wryly, 'It is, generally speaking, hardly my domain'. He was too passionate for the dreaming romantic mood, too stockily Russian for the languid poet.

During that first season with the Bolshoi he was happier with his other roles all of which had strong folk elements—the stonecutter in Grigorovitch's *The Stone Flower*, a popular moral dance-drama; Ivan the fool in Radunsky's *The Little Humpbacked Horse* with choreography based on stylized national dance.

In 1959, still generally considered to be a *demi-caractère* dancer he set off on his first tour abroad to the United States, Canada, China and Austria, where he was awarded a gold medal at the Festival of Youth and Students.

The tour was a revelation for Vasiliev. He discovered that there were significant differences in national balletic styles, and that as well as showing off the Russian style, he could also learn from the companies he saw.

On this, and subsequent tours abroad, the dancers were more than merely discouraged from watching Western performances. The KGB was always in attendance, and some of the dancers themselves were (and are) members. During the 1963 and 1965 visits to England, company members were specifically told not to attend Nureyev performances at the Royal Opera House, Covent Garden. Whether or not Vasiliev and other principals received special dispensation, they were certainly there in the stalls and the crush bar, and in 1975, in an interview for the American *Dance Magazine*, Vasiliev was quoted as saying, 'I think Nureyev did a lot for Western ballet. Everything that he got from the Russian school he brought here, and developed it: expressiveness, clarity and his strength—something of an animal, but a beautiful animal.'

What struck Vasiliev most was the Western emphasis on feet and legs, both in class and in performance. In the Russian school everything is used as an instrument of expression. 'The whole body is dancing, from the toes to the end of the fingertips.'

Vladimir Vasiliev demonstrating his brilliant panache in the leaping step known as brisés volés.

After returning from his first tour abroad Vasiliev started to take class with Alexei Yermolayev, who had been a principal dancer with the Bolshoi since 1930, but had just retired. There are times when an extraordinary rapport between teacher and student acts as a life-changing catalyst, and this is exactly what happened when Yermolayev began to coach the 20-year-old Vasiliev for the role of Basilio in *Don Quixote*. Until now the part had been played as a superficial joker and womanizer, but between them they evolved a character with warmth and reality, investing him with extraordinary bravura leaps and jumps which were wholly in keeping with the interpretation. Audiences were dazzled by the virtuosity and brilliance and Vasiliev was established as a star.

Yermolayev now taught Vasiliev Frondoso in *Laurencia*, based on Lope de Vega's tragedy *Fuente Ovejuno*, a ballet not seen in the West, although Nureyev staged the *pas de six* from it at the Royal Ballet in 1965.* It had been choreographed in 1939 by Vachtang Chaboukiani, one of Russia's greatest dancers who had twice won the Stalin Prize, but in the 1960s it seemed somewhat old-fashioned. There was less scope for change than in *Don Quixote*, but those that Vasiliev and Yermolayev contrived brought standing ovations night after night.

By 1962 Vasiliev had partnered Ulanova, Lepeshinskaya, Plisetskaya and Timofeyeva, the leading company ballerinas, and he now went on to win acclaim on foreign tours to America, Canada, Great Britain and France, where he received the Nijinsky Prize for the Best Dancer of the Year. The same year he won the Gold Medal at Varna. At home he danced Albrecht in *Giselle*, and once more with Yermolayev as his teacher and mentor, he brought new dimensions to a familiar role. The cynical seducer of the innocent peasant girl was replaced by a young man genuinely in love, torn between social status and inner passion, with Giselle's death compelling him to acknowledge his responsibility. In the second act of the ballet, Albrecht meets the ghosts of women betrayed by love, the revengeful Wilis, driving men to dance until they die from exhaustion. It is Giselle, risen from her newly-dug grave, who saves him, and Vasiliev choreographed his own variation to convey remorse and self-loathing bordering on a death wish. As morning dawns and the spirits fade, he is left tormented in an interpretation far beyond the traditional stereotype, intellectually founded on a proper psychological basis. Not surprisingly the audiences were stimulated and thrilled by innovations refreshingly free from the artistic strait-jacket.

Albrecht was followed by Menjun in a work not really known outside Russia, *Leili and Menjun*, choreographed by Kassian Goleizovsky, in which Vasiliev

* With Nerina, Sibley, Park, Nureyev, Gable and Usher.

displayed oriental plasticity and virtuoso turns and jumps in, among other highly charged scenes, a mad sequence in a desert. Again he delighted the public and by 1964 his combination of classical bravura and dramatic projection had made him something of a legend.

1964 was, as it turned out, a significant year for both Vasiliev and the company. It was the year in which Yuri Grigorovitch took control of the Bolshoi. Dancer, choreographer and now artistic director, Grigorovitch was considered by many to be unimaginative, unswervingly towing the party line. He was shortly to marry Tatiana Bessmertnova, a soloist with the company who was to become one of its major ballerinas.

Initially the relationship between the two men was equable, even promising. Grigorovitch's *Nutcracker* in 1965 provided Vasiliev with a dual role to please the public, and records show that the metamorphosis from the mechanical nutcracker toy to handsome prince was spectacular and magical. This was followed by Siegfried in the company's standard *Swan Lake*, which Vasiliev confessed privately was a long way from his own conception.

In the meantime Grigorovitch was working on *Spartacus*, a work redolent of early Hollywood kitsch which wowed the Moscow audiences and indeed those abroad, by its scenes with massed male dancers. The physique and strength of the Russian men was tremendously impressive, and the choreographic rhythms built up a kind of ritualistic excitement. Vasiliev brought his superman qualities to drama as he danced in chains, and a tender lyricism to his *pas de deux* with Phrygia danced by Maximova. As always real life love added a *frisson* to an enacted stage version, and audiences responded.

Perhaps it was his dissatisfaction with the choreographic confines that inspired Vasiliev to turn to creating his own ballet. In 1968 his first work, *Icarus*, to music by Sergei Slonimsky, was over-weighted with theatrical tricks and he was dissatisfied with the result. That same year the company toured Italy, where he was subsequently to guest on many occasions. In 1969 Grigorovitch brought the Bolshoi and *Spartacus* to London, drawing—as this company always does—spectators who never attend ballet performances at any other time. The Bolshoi name has the aura of one of the wonders of the world. Whatever the actual quality of its repertoire, designs and dancers at the time, it stands for 'biggest and best' and Westerners will pay astronomical prices for tickets irrespective of what they are going to see. This is not to say that the company does not have extraordinary principal dancers trained to the highest world standards and demonstrating breathtaking ability, but the artistic direction has not kept pace with the ideas, visual presentation and invention of contemporary ballet outside

Left Vladimir Vasiliev in the solo variation from the Don Quixote pas de deux.

Below Vladimir Vasiliev in the title role of Spartacus, partnering his wife, the great Bolshoi ballerina Ekaterina Maximova.

the Iron Curtain. Even the classics are 'out of date'; the mime indulges in silent-film eye rolling; the costumes are tasteless and zips are visible on shiny nylon bodices; the wigs are frequently unintentionally comic. For some reason, because it is the Bolshoi, critics who are outspoken and ascerbic over the faults of other companies, refrain from pointing out the shortcomings. Vasiliev however has not been afraid to speak out on his home ground, and for many years he has battled with the autocratic Grigorovitch.

It was the simplistic ideology of Grigorovitch's *Ivan the Terrible* in 1974 that brought the conflict into the open arena. Moscow intelligentsia found the theme to be an abject surrender to the Soviet regime, and a subjugation of the idea of freedom. With prima ballerina, Maya Plisetskaya, Vasiliev formed a determined opposition which reached its climax when, as an outspoken member of the Bolshoi Art Committee, he harshly criticized Grigorovitch's full length *Angara*, another receptacle for socialist realism.

Outside Russia, Vasiliev remains loyal. When discussing their working relationship he speaks in generous terms. 'If it's a completely new production, then it's a joint work, because the choreographer works like a sculptor. With Grigorovitch, the idea of his ballet as a whole will be already set but, nevertheless, when he comes to the first sessions with the dancers, it's like a second birth; the interpretative artist stimulates him.' He added, in this same interview with Tobi Tobias in *Dance Magazine*, 'As for choreography, in his new works, Grigorovitch tries to combine the epic mode, which is his natural bent, with the traditions of classical Russian ballet.' Praising the classical technique of the company male dancers as being even more streamlined and athletic, he gently implied that the famous expressiveness had declined under the present regime.

Vasiliev enjoys a special position within the USSR's artistic framework. Lenin Prize-holder, Merited Artist of the Soviet Union, opponent of established order, he dances in Paris and Rome and Buenos Aires with indiginous companies as a guest as might any Western star. As a deputy of the USSR Supreme Council he has, it seems, unlimited freedom to select his own foreign tours and to collaborate with foreign choreographers. His association with Maurice Bejart and his (then) Ballet of the Twentieth Century continued over a sustained period. 'His audacity will never cease to amaze me!' Vasiliev was highly acclaimed in Bejart's *Romeo and Juliet*, greatly admired his *Sacre du Printemps*, and in the summer of 1979 astonished Paris audiences expecting the usual Bolshoi fare by showing three Bejart works (*Isadora*, a *pas de deux* from *Romeo and Juliet* and *Leda*) and three of his own (a revised version of his early *Icarus*, *Les Promenades* and an abstract work to Mozart's Symphony No 40).

He treads a fine line and it is difficult to discern his attitude towards plotless ballets. He has spoken of an inclination towards 'pure dance for the sake of dance' but also expounded on the need for plot, an 'informing idea' so that the choreographer's viewpoint is clear to the audience. 'Without this, abstract ballet is absolutely cold and mechanical, with nothing behind it, nothing interesting about it but its shape.' Certainly the Russians want a socialist statement from a choreographer and even so privileged an artist as Vasiliev would need to conform. In 1980 he stayed within the accepted formula with a too literal Macbeth, with ensemble scenes on the famous Bolshoi scale showing a choreographic talent for spectacle but no distinctive personal style. What did emerge was the intellectual concept, with the witches (three male dancers on point) instigating the action throughout.

Vasiliev's avid interest in all aspects of contemporary dance has certainly not led to emulation. Of the Americans his personal taste leans towards Alvin Ailey and Paul Taylor but Balanchine he finds cold, calling him 'a separate page in the history of classical dance'.

While he is forthcoming with his professional opinions, Vasiliev retains Russian reserve when asked about his personal life. He is still married to Maximova and they are said to be a devoted couple, although there are no children. Her attempted suicide remains an enigma and with the absence of a gutter press on Hollywood lines, fans have speculated pointlessly. To Western interviewers he is charming and thoughtful in his answers to questions that must seem irrelevant. Yes, he likes tennis, volleyball, swimming, driving fast, playing chess with his wife. He emerges as an all-rounder, painting—his pictures have been exhibited—listening to music when he has the time. He has even written a few stories.

In the late 1980s it seems as if Russia is at last catching up with Vasiliev. While retaining strong national identity, he has seen the need to reject the outdated and to move forward positively with personal freedom still serving an ideal. Classical ballet will be forever in his debt.

Natalia Makarova is one of the great trio of defecting dancers from the Kirov Ballet in Leningrad—the other two being Rudolf Nureyev and Mikhail Baryshnikov—who have immeasurably enriched the Western world of dance. Ninette de Valois once remarked: 'We [i.e., the Royal Ballet] must always look to the Kirov as our pedagogues', and there is some irony in the fact that the repressive Soviet system drove three of the company's greatest artists into exile in the West, where their quest for new roles and new horizons made them role-models for so many aspiring young dancers of the free world.

Makarova was born on 21 November 1940, on the eve of Soviet Russia's entry into the Second World War. Her family were members of the intelligentsia, her grandfather being an architect who stimulated her early interest in painting and theatre. Makarova's father was killed early in the war and her mother soon remarried; her stepfather was the only father she ever knew. She describes her childhood as 'joyless and hungry wanderings around towns and villages of the Yaroslav region', the bleak plain some 150 miles north-east of Moscow. The joylessness and hunger were no doubt the result of the desperate privations of the war, although it is doubtful if she suffered the poverty and destitution endured by Nureyev in his childhood.

After the war the family was resettled in Leningrad. She found the academic syllabus of her grammar school boring—which she overcame with typical rebelliousness by reading Jules Verne in class, for which she was punished—although she did well at her studies. She remembers two aspects of her personality (which have not changed) as 'curiosity and perfectionism', and it was the first of these traits that led her to enroll at the Palace of Pioneers for the gymnastic class; inexplicably, she ended up in the ballet class. Equally inexplicably—because she seemed not to be able to manage the steps she was taught—her teacher there suggested she should enroll at the celebrated Vaganova School. By herself she found the establishment on Rossi Street where, after a physical examination, she was accepted as a pupil. Her parents were horrified—the bourgeois attitude to a life on the stage still remained, even if the social strata had been officially obliterated. But Makarova threw screaming tantrums until her family gave in and she was admitted to the ballet school. She was placed into the newly formed Experimental Class, created for war-children who had not only suffered through malnutrition, and therefore did not have the stamina and muscular strength requisite for ballet training, but who had also made a late start for one reason or another. Makarova was given a course which condensed the nine-year curriculum into six years.

Partly because of this rushed training, and partly because her muscles were

'soft' by nature, Makarova found that her technique was splendid for the Romantic repertoire—*Giselle, La Sylphide, Les Sylphides*—but unable to cope with the steely strength necessary for the great Petipa classics—*The Sleeping Beauty, Swan Lake, La Bayadère*. It was not until years later, after she had defected to the West, that she was able to cope with the technical demands of such ballets.

And yet it was the imperial tradition of the Tsar's St Petersburg ballet company, the impeccable classical style, untainted by arid concepts of Socialist Realism that infected all the other Soviet arts, with which Makarova became imbued. If she found the virtuoso roles too difficult to cope with as a young graduate of the Vaganova School, she nevertheless absorbed its aristocratic teaching— the pedagoguery that de Valois insists is the classical heritage of our own Royal Ballet.

Makarova was taught by Elena Shiripina and Natalia Dudinskaya and has described herself as 'an impossible student, always going around with my head in the clouds'. She graduated in 1959, dancing the adagio from the second act of *Giselle* with Nikita Dolgushin as her partner.

Entering the *corps de ballet* of the Kirov, Makarova felt 'an overwhelming, paralysing fear'. She was desperately shy and in total awe of the principal dancers. Whether this inhibiting sense of inferiority was what produced her inability to conform to the necessary mass movement, whether it was the same dreamy forgetfulness that she had shown as a student, or whether it was her instinctive individuality that produced her 'hilarious mistakes', it is not easy to tell; but she was certainly not intended to remain a *corps* dancer. She was singled out by Boris Fenster, Director of the company, and given solo roles. Then, on 27 December 1959, only a few months after joining the illustrious company, she danced her first complete performance of Giselle, with Dolgushin as her partner. It was the beginning of an association with the ballet that has predominated over all others, a work which was completely compatible with her physical characteristics and which, she has said, has given her her greatest successes and creative satisfaction.

Her first performance was both spontaneous and against all tradition. The choreography was 'in her feet', as the saying is, so she did not have to concentrate unduly on the steps; her interpretation of Giselle was lively and coquettish, making eyes at Albrecht—a far cry from the shy, frail, simple village girl with which audiences are usually presented. She 'overdid the mad scene and died much

Natalia Makarova exemplifying the superb Kirov classical style as Kitri in the Don Quixote pas de deux.

too theatrically'. In the second act her instinctive rebelliousness was, of course, somewhat more in keeping with the character of the dead girl who, as a Wili, defies the commands of her Queen and sustains her beloved Albrecht against the Wilis' malevolence.

Makarova's independent approach to the role of Giselle was symptomatic of her approach to life as well as to the aesthetic problems of her art. Her quest for truth in a role has led her to give widely varying interpretations of the parts she has played—including the nineteenth-century classics—and it is significant that she often speaks and writes of 'the soul' when discussing her dancing: 'The dance, and every ballet lesson as well, is like a confession . . . for to become a ballerina means to bring into ideal balance the essentially instrumental, physical possibilities of your capricious, imperfect body with the possibilities of your soul, which is eternally renewing itself and constantly demanding new expression.'

At the Kirov Makarova was 'loaded down' with the entire repertory, including early melodramatic Soviet ballets such as *Masquerade* and *The Fountain of Bakhchisarai*. In *Masquerade*, by Fenster, she danced the role of Nina who, like Desdemona, dies from the machinations of a jealous husband. As Maria, in *The Fountain of Bakhchisarai*, she played a Polish princess who, loved by a Tartan khan, is stabbed to death by the jealous first wife of the harem. Makarova was 'bored to death' by these roles and could find no way to imbue them with life, either for herself or her audiences.

As a means of escaping from the feeling of stagnation she began to identify herself with the work of Leonid Yakobson whose 'rebellious' experimentation, as well as provoking the suspicions and displeasure of the authorities, found an affinity with Makarova's own questing personality. She danced in a brief work of his, *The Kiss*, an erotic miniature inspired by Rodin's sculpture and danced to music by Debussy, and in a more ambitious ballet, *The Bedbug*, loosely based on Mayakovsky's play. Working on that ballet was 'a turning point', the awareness of a choreographer creating something from the freedom of his own imagination, not held within the rigid structure of an artistic policy laid down by Party chiefs. The role of Zoya is that of a young, naïve girl who is betrayed by her dolt of a husband—something of a latter-day Giselle—but instead of the peasant clothes Makarova appeared in a 'faded, ill-fitting little dress, in low heels, and with a short, boyish hair-cut'. She says she loved both the 'brazenness and the shy vulnerability' of the role.

Later, Makarova appeared in Yakobson's *New Love*, to music by Ravel, and in a more conventionally fairy-tale work, *Country of Wonders*, for which she was named the best Soviet ballerina of the year 1967. She had also begun to rehearse a role in a highly controversial ballet by Jakobson, *The Twelve*, which greatly annoyed the Party censors, but she had to withdraw because of the pressure of work imposed by the regular repertoire—in particular, *Swan Lake*. Like so many ballerinas, Makarova had great trouble with the infamous 32 *fouettés* of the Black Swan *pas de deux* of the third act. At her first performance she finished the *fouettés* upstage in a rear wing—'after the first 10 bars no one could see me any more'. At her last performance (in 1970, before leaving for a British tour) she made three separate attempts at the variation while the orchestra stopped, astonished. 'Only in the West was I freed from my Swan complex,' she has said.

Her commitment to the work of Yakobson brought disapproval from the authorities. He created a new ballet for her, *A Passing Beauty*, another of his 'miniatures', this time based on a Picasso motif. The ballet received just two performances at the Leningrad Conservatory. After the second performance she received a telephone call from the Party *Obkom* (the State Party Commander) insisting that she did not continue with the work 'in consideration of her future career'. Makarova was banished back to the classics which, more and more, she found to be suffocating museum pieces.

Even so, she was coached in these virtuoso roles by some of the greatest ballerinas of the age who, even if they represented the stultifying official approach to the art, nevertheless taught her all the bravura techniques so necessary to the interpretation of such parts. This technical know-how remains 'in the feet' throughout a dancer's life; it may need constant practice and polishing, it may need frequent reminders from teachers and coaches, but, once acquired, the knowledge is there to be called upon at will. Conversely, an idea can occur in the subconscious—so psychiatrists tell us—that, for some time, lies dormant, unaccepted and unacknowledged by the conscious mind. It is probable, therefore, that the idea of defecting to the West had occurred to Makarova long before she acted upon it. She had before her the example of Nureyev, who had made his decision some nine years previously, and her utter boredom with the repertoire of the Kirov, her awareness that she was giving opaque, uninspired performances, had distressed her as early as 1967. The Kirov tour that included London in 1970 proved the catalyst that crystallized a decision that had as much importance for the art of ballet in the West as it had for the ballerina who made it.

Makarova left for London in a state of great depression. The role of Juliet in an impressionistic one-act version of *Romeo and Juliet* by Igor Tchernishov to the symphonic poem by Berlioz had been forbidden by the Kirov Director, Konstantin Sergeyev, because of its 'formalism', 'eroticism', and so on. Yet, soon after, Irina Kolpakova, 'thanks to her Party card and connections in high places', managed to get a single performance of it. In London the Kirov performed at the Royal Festival Hall where Makarova danced Giselle and in several classical *pas de deux*. Throughout the trip she spent time enjoying the material advantages of the capital—she was even given permission and money from the Kirov to buy a British car—and seeing friends she had made during her two previous visits with the company. At the end of the season, at dinner with Irina and Vladimir Rodzianko, Irina suddenly said that Makarova was 'destroying herself' by remaining with the Kirov and that she should stay in London. At first Makarova laughed at the suggestion then, when she had had some moments to think about the full implications of the idea—leaving her mother and her friends, her career with the famous Kirov—when, perhaps, her subconscious, unspoken thoughts had been given utterance by someone else, she started to cry. After 15 minutes she stopped weeping and said, quietly, 'Call the police. I am ready.'

Two friendly young constables responded to the telephone call and, after asking Makarova if her decision was final and receiving an affirmative answer, took her to a police station. Permission to stay was given the next morning.

Somewhat naïvely, perhaps, Makarova thought that she might be offered a position with the Royal Ballet, but that company does not usually accept dancers from outside the organization and Equity is generally strict about such matters— otherwise the company would have been glad to welcome such brilliant dancers as, for example, Marcia Haydée and Richard Cragun, stars of the Stuttgart Ballet who had trained at, and graduated from, the Royal Ballet School. Even Nureyev had to accept the status of 'permanent guest artist'. And that, under the MacMillan regime, is what Makarova became for a number of seasons.

Immediately after her defection Makarova received a series of letters from her former colleagues—persuasive, bitter, faintly threatening—just as Nureyev had done. There were also many newspaper interviews, given through Vladimir Rodzianko as her interpreter. Makarova survived all the hysteria and hype, the threats and pleadings, feeling that she had made the right, irrevocable, decision. Her first performance was on television dancing first in Fokine's *The Dying Swan* and then, with Nureyev, the Black Swan *pas de deux* from *Swan Lake* (she would have been forgiven for wondering if that is what she had left Russia for!), about which she was less than happy, calling it an 'eternal reproach'.

The first positive offer of real substance came in a telegram from American Ballet Theatre, a company which Makarova had seen and liked while it was performing in London. She arrived in New York in the autumn of 1970 and, of course, virtually alone (Rodzianko was, initially, her interpreter and manager) in a strange environment and without any command of the language. But her resilience, her determination and courage surmounted all the difficulties, not least because she was convinced she had made the right decision for her future.

For her debut with ABT Makarova chose—predictably—*Giselle*, although the production was vastly different from the one she had been accustomed to. Her projected partner was Erik Bruhn, arguably the finest *premier danseur* produced by the West at that time, a superb classical stylist and a strong, considerate partner. On the eve of the performance, however, Bruhn sustained a serious injury and, in Makarova's own words, 'this was the perfect moment to panic'.

But then along came her 'Prince Charming': Ivan Nagy, a Hungarian-born dancer, 'handsome, well-mannered, enthusiastic and with sturdy partnering arms'. After leaving Hungary he had danced with Washington National Ballet and New York City Ballet before joining ABT in 1968. He was—certainly at that time—a perfect partner for Makarova, not just in his fine stage presence and with an excellent technique, but also as a calm, solicitous, emotional anchor, and she began to relate to him 'as a brother'.

Her partnership with Bruhn was fulfilled at a later date. They danced *Giselle* together with great success, both the full ballet and the *pas de deux* from Act II, also Fokine's *Les Sylphides*, August Bournonville's full-length early nineteenth-century Romantic classic *La Sylphide*, Alvin Ailey's *The River*, and four of Antony Tudor's great works, *Lilac Garden*, *Pillar of Fire*, *Dark Elegies* and *Romeo and Juliet*.

The Romantic ballets, *La Sylphide* and *Giselle*, presented no great technical difficulties, Makarova's 'soft' muscularity being ideal for the delicate, ethereal heroines of both works, and Bruhn, being a Dane brought up in the Bournonville tradition (Bournonville created a great repertoire of works for the Royal Danish Ballet during the nineteenth century, most of which have been carefully preserved), was of immense help to her in perfecting the correct stylistic manner and technique.

Ailey's *The River* and the Tudor ballets presented a number of interpretive problems, however. Like most classical dancers, Makarova had great difficulty in acquiring the requisite rhythmic freedom for a jazz ballet like *The River*. It goes against all the highly formulated, stylistically elaborate manner of classicism, demanding a plasticity and spontaneity that is the antithesis of the classical *haute école*. In order to study jazz dancing, to get the 'feel' of the rhythmic response, Makarova and Bruhn visited a jazz discotheque where she received 'some sense of syncopated beat' that she retained until she made her debut in the ballet. Afterwards, a critic wrote that she danced jazz as if she had been doing it all her life, which was flattering, but it was an imposed ability, like an actor adopting an accent which is alien to him.

If Ailey's work had presented purely physical problems, Tudor's ballets were full of intellectual and psychological difficulties—as they have been for so many dancers. When Makarova first met Tudor at ABT she was immediately impressed with him, although well aware that he was generally respected and feared because of his relentlessly caustic manner towards the dancers he worked with, thinking nothing of humiliating them with sarcastic remarks during rehearsals. Despite her difficulty with the language—many of Tudor's acid comments were simply not understood—Makarova defended her reasons for interpreting a character in a particular way with considerable asperity so that their rehearsal encounters often became a verbal duel. Makarova and Tudor developed a mutual respect for one another, although he remained typically enigmatic in his reactions to her performances of his work. This seemingly diffident response could, with Tudor, be token approval; if he did not like something he would more often than not resort to some damning, pithy comment.

Tudor was the creator of the modern 'psychological' ballet in which, combined with the formal vocabulary of classical dance, a glance, a gesture, could indicate a wealth of meaning, what was going on in the mind of a character, hinting at subtle relationships, suggesting emotional turmoil beneath a formal, composed exterior. In his famous *Lilac Garden* (originally created in England in 1936 under the title *Jardin aux Lilas*) Makarova danced the role of Caroline, the young wife-to-be who, at a party, meets again the man she really loves; at the same reception is the woman who is her fiancé's ex-mistress. This Proustian situation is revealed in brief lovers' meetings, in hints of regret at what must be, of remembrance of things past, where social convention forbids the expression of deep emotion. Makarova had great difficulty with this role (she was also rehearsing other ballets at the same time) in which her rather more extrovert Russian temperament was at odds with the essentially British emotional restraint.

In response to Makarova's pleas Tudor spent three hours rehearsing with her *at home*, where, she says, she learnt much more than in the studio rehearsals. Tudor made little comment about her performance but later, when the role was being learnt by another dancer, he said, 'Watch her [Makarova], see how she moves—that's the way to do it.' Nevertheless, Makarova comments that she 'never came to terms with the ballet and probably never danced it to the best of my abilities'.

Another Tudor character who eluded Makarova was Hagar in *Pillar of Fire*, created for the great American dramatic ballerina Norah Kaye in 1942. Danced to Arnold Schoenberg's tone poem *Transfigured Night*, the narrative illustrates Hagar's concern that the man she loves will prefer her flirtatious younger sister. In desperation she gives herself to a stranger, but is forgiven by her real lover who reveals great sympathy for her anguish. Makarova confesses she saw nothing in this character but 'an embittered old spinster', and did not feel 'natural' in the role. After a number of performances Makarova found inspiration in the film of Chekhov's *The Lady with the Little Dog*. It was a highly personal inspiration: 'The sublime expression which Savina, who played the lead, conveyed with her clear eyes, longing for love while disbelieving in it . . . I simply felt the expression of those eyes physically, and everything fell into place.' After her next performance Tudor said, 'Now you're doing what you have to.'

Makarova also danced in Tudor's one-act version of *Romeo and Juliet*, to music

Natalia Makarova demonstrating her superb technique as Odile in Swan Lake. *This photograph is from a television production by the BBC.*

by Delius, but found it unrewarding, and in his beautiful, intense, deceptively simple *Dark Elegies*, based on Mahler's *Kindertotenlieder* (Songs on the Death of Children), which also presented interpretive problems.

Balanchine's *Theme and Variations*, set to the final movement of Tchaikovsky's Suite No 3, presented problems of a purely technical nature—as his works often do to dancers who have not grown up with his highly idiosyncratic neo-classical style. And being a plotless ballet there was no emotional expression or narrative theme with which to associate; the movement was all. 'But I personally cannot accept this . . . as an aesthetic credo,' Markova says. 'I prefer ballets in which there is room for an interpretation, where I can partially express my own human experience, in the hope it will find a response in someone's heart.'

But if all these ballets presented problems—aesthetic, emotional, and technical—that was, after all, why Makarova had come to the West; to be challenged by works that simply would not have been allowed in Soviet Russia. These difficulties were compounded by the wildly hectic pace that was also at complete variance with the professional lifestyle of the Kirov where, far from rehearsing several ballets simultaneously, and rehearsing for eight hours followed by an evening performance, merely 'to speak of a rehearsal on the same day as a performance would have been blasphemy'.

This demand, commonly accepted by dancers in the West, who have grown used not only to the hectic pace but the need to switch from one style to another within a single programme, was something that Makarova has never been able to come to terms with, feeling that it can only lead to a superficial interpretation of a given role. It was a feeling which, after two years, led her to leave ABT—a decision arrived at after a long dinner-table conversation with the famous impresario Sol Hurok.

For the next two years Makarova engaged in an equally exhausting series of guest performances around the world—*Swan Lake* and *Giselle* in South Africa, John Taras's version of *Rite of Spring* at La Scala, Milan, *Coppelia* in Berlin, and engagements in Stockholm, Munich, Zurich and Paris—it was as if Makarova needed to convince herself that she was really wanted in the West. In Reggio she danced in Maria Callas's production of *I Vespri Siciliani* (it was Callas's debut as an opera producer) and the two women got on well together, both recognizing each other as a supremely dedicated artiste in her own sphere.

In June 1972, Makarova danced as a guest artist with the Royal Ballet in London, giving two performances of *Giselle* with Anthony Dowell as Albrecht and two of *Swan Lake* with Donald MacLeary as Prince Siegfried. Makarova feels that these performances were not entirely satisfactory, mainly because of having to adjust not only to new partners but also to productions which were, in essence, very different from the ones she had danced in before, both with the Kirov and with ABT. Compromise is rarely successful in art, and for a ballerina such as Makarova, who had her own very definite conception of the roles, it resulted in performances that were only patchily effective.

Greater success and satisfaction came a year later when she tackled a work by MacMillan for the first time, his full-length *Romeo and Juliet*. Despite having to learn the role in a week she was immediately at home, not only with the very demanding choreography but also with the character of Juliet. Here, for the first time in the West, was a modern conception of a fully rounded character, something which would allow Makarova her full range of expression, a part which—as with nearly all MacMillan's major works—leaves plenty of room for the dancer to create her individual interpretation, wholly without the years of traditional accretions that are attached to the classics.

With Nureyev as Romeo, Makarova's Juliet was a tremendous success, her greatest and most satisfying triumph since she had defected, a performance that was received with rapture by both audience and critics. It was the more remarkable because she and Nureyev had danced together for the first time only a fortnight before, in a performance of *The Sleeping Beauty*, and their partnership had not been entirely harmonious.

The following year Makarova returned to ABT—not to dance, but to produce the Kingdom of the Shades scene from *La Bayadère*. The undertaking gave her some sleepless nights inasmuch that she was reviving the ballet from memory, and the memories only came fitfully. Also she found some difficulty in imparting Petipa's conception of the Shades (spirits of Indian temple dancers) to the young dancers of the *corps de ballet*, dancers who, unlike Makarova, had not had the nineteenth-century classics as the very cornerstone of their training since their very first years in ballet school. As the first night approached Makarova was in agony of apprehension. While this was still in preparation—and, in fact, while Makarova was still in London—she received a telephone call from Mikhail Baryshnikov telling her that he too, during an appearance with the Kirov in Canada, had decided to defect to the West. Realizing what tremendous emotional pressures he must be suffering and that he needed all the support and encouragement he could get, she undertook to speak to Lucia Chase, Director of ABT, and ask that she be allowed to dance her forthcoming performance of Giselle with the company with Baryshnikov as her partner.

So it was arranged, and their first *Giselle* together took New York by storm. They also danced the *pas de deux* from *Don Quixote*, a virtuoso show-piece, with equal success and this partnership—one that was to be repeated frequently—was not only brilliant in itself but also served to introduce Baryshnikov to American audiences at a time when he was in need of psychological support.

The first night of *La Bayadère* with Cynthia Harvey dancing the principal role of Nikiya was also a great success; 1974 was turning out to be a year of memorable triumphs for Makarova, a year which fully justified all the risks she had taken by detaching herself from her homeland and abandoning stability for artistic and political freedom.

Back in London, during the autumn season of 1974, Makarova had further triumphs in two of MacMillan's greatest works, the full-length *Manon* and his one-act masterpiece, *Song of the Earth*. Of the part of Manon Makarova has said, 'Probably no other of my roles in the West means as much to me as Manon . . . whose character I see as one of the most enchanting and complex in French literature', and certainly her portrayal of this *femme fatale*, the woman for whom the young student Des Grieux lies and cheats and murders, was both marvellously danced and the character illumined with great clarity and understanding. The performance, with Anthony Dowell as Des Grieux, also served to develop and consolidate their understanding of one another as artists—it was the beginning of a partnership that was to be one of the most rewarding of both their careers. Dowell's natural reserve, his 'inherent gentlemanliness', developed into a friendship that allowed both dancers to extend their understanding of each other's artistic aims and ideals. There was a rapport between them that projected beyond the footlights, in a mutual appreciation of each other's way of working, of eradicating any false or easy approach to a problem. This understanding was apparent in subsequent appearances in *Giselle* with Dowell, after the constraint Makarova had felt during their first performances together.

Another MacMillan work with which Makarova found great affinity was *Song of the Earth*. An acknowledged masterpiece, danced to Mahler's great symphonic song cycle, its theme of a woman coming to terms with the inevitability of death appealed to her sense of the metaphysical. The choreography for all three major protagonists—The Man, The Woman, and The Messenger of Death—is exhaustingly difficult, but Makarova surmounted all the technical hurdles because of her belief in the theme and its wonderful realization in the choreography. Subsequently she said, '*Song of the Earth* confirmed my real connection with the Royal Ballet', and of all the modern ballets that she has ever danced it was MacMillan's works which have given her the most satisfaction, the greatest feeling of artistic achievement.

Another modern work with which Makarova felt an intuitive sympathy was

Glen Tetley's *Voluntaries*. Created as a tribute to John Cranko after the Director of the Stuttgart Ballet's untimely death, it is another ballet in which the theme of 'death, by death subdued' is revealed in demanding but beautiful choreography. Tetley's version of the *Rite of Spring* proved more difficult because Makarova found the choreography more formalistic and mechanical, but she undertook to dance it because, once again, she was primarily concerned with extending her ballet vocabulary.

Throughout the 1970s and the early 1980s Makarova did just that, dividing her main engagements between ABT and the Royal Ballet but also guesting with several other major ballet companies throughout the world. In April 1977 she was instrumental in reviving a version of Prokoviev's *Romeo and Juliet* by Igor Tchernikov which had been summarily cancelled by the Kirov authorities. She was invited to do so by Tchernikov's ex-wife, Elena Kittel-Tchernishova, who, having been involved in the original production, was resurrecting it for the Maryland Ballet in Baltimore, under the direction of Kathleen Crofton. With Ivan Nagy as her Romeo it must be accounted more of a curiosity than anything else and it is probable that Makarova felt that, by being involved with the production, she was making a personal reply to the suppressive actions of her native company.

During this period Makarova determined to master the technical difficulties of *The Sleeping Beauty*, with its academic brilliance, and *Swan Lake*, with its accent on lyrical drama. This she did with a characteristic determination and thoroughness, overcoming all the technical problems and giving an unusual depth to the interpretation of the roles. Her portrayals of Odette-Odile in *Swan Lake* were, in particular, memorable performances, with Anthony Dowell as a sensitive and passionate Prince Siegfried.

In 1977 Makarova married Edward Karker, an electronics executive, in San Francisco. It was an impressive ceremony, performed with all the pomp and panoply of the Russian Orthodox Church, and the ceremonial crown was held above Makarova's head by Baryshnikov. On 1 February 1978, Makarova gave birth to a son, André-Michel (Andrushka). Three and a half months later she was dancing brilliantly in Jerome Robbins's *Other Dances* in New York, partnered by Baryshnikov. In that same season she also danced in *La Sylphide* and *Voluntaries* and made her first appearance as Kitri in a new full-length version of a rumbustious nineteenth-century classic, *Don Quixote*, giving the character a flamboyant abandon and finding much mischievous humour in the part. All this despite a feeling that she was having to fight the physical constraints of her muscularity, and enduring fits of depression brought on by the thought that her body was no longer as pliant and responsive as it had been. But audiences and critics gave her rapturous receptions and reviews and were in general accord that she was one of the few great ballerinas of the age.

In 1980 Makarova produced the full-length, four-act version of *La Bayadère* for ABT—the first time the entire work had been staged in the West. It was a great success and a welcome addition to the company's repertoire of classics. During the mid-1980s there were a number of rumours and statements that Makarova had retired from dancing, all of which proved unfounded as she continued to dance with ABT and a number of other companies around the world. In this period she made the role of the heroine, Tatiana, in John Cranko's *Onegin* very much her own, dancing it for a number of seasons with London Festival Ballet and receiving the London Evening Standard Ballet Award for her interpretation of the part. She also danced the role with great success in the National Ballet of Canada's production.

In 1983 she made her debut in musical comedy, performing the part of the volatile, tempestuous Russian ballerina in *On Your Toes*, with choreography by Balanchine. For this performance on Broadway she was given a coveted Tony Award—something she prized particularly as it recognized her emergence into a new genre and her ability to cope with a speaking role. Her performance in the London production at the Palace Theatre also received great acclaim.

In 1987 Makarova appeared in a BBC TV series entitled *Ballerina*, as well as a TV film in which she was coached by the celebrated Russian teacher Irina Jakobson. In both features her highly photogenic qualities were in evidence, together with a compelling personality—described by one critic as 'a combination of Greta Garbo's mystery with Marlene Dietrich's glamour'. Makarova herself has spoken of wanting to extend her acting career on stage and film. Whatever the future might hold, however, nothing will eradicate memories of her as a great ballerina, supreme in Romantic works like *La Sylphide* and *Giselle*, superlative in *Swan Lake* and *La Bayadère*, brilliant in *Don Quixote*, memorably moving in a wide range of the modern repertoire—particularly in MacMillan's *Romeo and Juliet*, *Manon*, and *Song of the Earth*, Glen Tetley's *Voluntaries*, and John Cranko's *Onegin*—performances which embodied both of those formidable characteristics, 'curiosity and perfectionism'.

There were already two Russian superstars, Nureyev and Makarova, who had defected to the West when Mikhail Baryshnikov gave the KGB the slip in Montreal. After a performance of *Don Quixote* he joined his young American girlfriend, Christina Berlin, and the following morning he requested asylum from the American Consulate. It was 29 June 1974.

The press, of course, made the most of it, paying more attention to the romance than to the good fortune of having a dancer of such calibre permanently on this side of the Iron Curtain. It was heralded that he defected for love, and the public learned that the couple had met in England during the 1970 Kirov tour. Christina had subsequently travelled to Russia to see him and they had managed to carry on a secret relationship. Gelsey Kirkland, the ballerina who has publicized her own affair with Mischa (as he is known to everyone), said that he proposed marriage to Christina shortly after the defection. True or false, the world knows he remains a bachelor, although he has a daughter, Alexandra, by the film actress Jessica Lange. He also has two much-loved dogs, Goulue and Katia, about whom he talks more freely than his human relationships. (Whoever else he left behind in Russia, there was certainly a white poodle called Foma.)

For any refugee—and defectors are amongst them, even if by choice—the effect of being cut off from past life must be traumatic. Baryshnikov, deserted by his mother when he was 12, had already experienced something of the defector's loneliness and sense of loss. Perhaps the misery of his early years made the decision to start in another country less complicated than for Nureyev, for instance, who until *glasnost* was not allowed to visit his mother for 26 years. When asked about his childhood, Baryshnikov, quoting someone else, said, 'Nothing is more sordid than childhood.'

He was born on 27 January 1948 in Riga, the capital of Latvia. His father was Nikolai Baryshnikov, a Soviet officer; his mother (Nikolai's second wife) Alexandra Kiseleva. In Russia he has a half-brother and sister from his father's first marriage. There is little information about the pre-student years, except that his father didn't think dancing was much of a career for his son, and it was his errant mother who was responsible for taking him along to ballet classes at the Riga dance school, where the syllabus was based on the one used in the Vaganova School in Leningrad. This was in 1960, so it must have been only a short time before she left the family. Nothing Baryshnikov has said or written since gives an indication of what happened to her, or whether she is still alive. It seems significant that although the wound never healed, his daughter bears her name. His father died in the late 1970s, but by this time had come to terms with his son's choice of career, for on being shown a copy of *Baryshnikov at Work*,

an autobiography, he said, 'My little son . . . my pride . . .'

In 1962 Baryshnikov graduated to the advanced class, and two years later moved to Leningrad to enroll in the Vaganova (Kirov) School and joined the class of the renowned teacher, Alexander Pushkin, who after his own dancing career with the company ended numbered among his pupils some of the Soviet Union's most outstanding male dancers, Rudolf Nureyev among them.

It was Pushkin who taught Baryshnikov for the next three years, during which time he won the Gold Medal in the junior category at Varna, the venue of the International Ballet Competition, the most distinguished in the contemporary world. A year later, in 1967, he joined the Kirov company as a soloist.

While he was a student Baryshnikov lived with others in an uncomfortable dormitory in a brick building on Pravda Street. It was close to Pushkin's home and he was often invited there by his teacher and his wife, Ksenia Iosifovna, and their friendship and hospitality helped to make those years happy. He is remembered then, and during his early years with the company, as being humorous, lively, and thirsty for all aspects of cultural life. He managed to attend all the new films, plays and ballets and to read the latest books, and this was an early warning that he would become frustrated by the limited cultural confines of the USSR. It is likely that the first visit abroad to London in 1970 planted the seed that was to flower four years later. The combination of an attractive American girl and the realization of artistic potential and scope in the West was enough to start the young man's mind moving in the direction of personal freedom. He could not have envisaged the welcome that lay ahead.

He did not fit easily into the usual categories of *danseur noble* or *demi-caractère*. On the one hand he possessed impeccable classical technique; on the other, he was small, compact, and slightly built. When on point most ballerinas were a head taller.

He made his debut with the Kirov in the Peasant *pas de deux* from *Giselle*. This was followed by the technically demanding role of the Blue Bird in *The Sleeping Beauty*, when the dancer scarcely seems to touch the ground as he emulates flight, and then by the romantic *Les Sylphides* with its glorious Chopin score and choreography by Fokine. There was also a concert programme which included, as such events almost always did, the show pieces from *Le Corsaire* and *Don Quixote*, expected by conservative Russian audiences.

Mikhail Baryshnikov's bravura technique combined dazzling virtuosity with perfect classical style. In this photograph the camera catches him in a superb jété from Jerome Robbins's Other Dances *first performed by Baryshnikov and Makarova at a gala in 1976.*

In 1969 he again walked off with a prize, this time the Nijinsky Prize in Moscow, for which he danced a piece choreographed especially for him by Leonid Jacobson, ballet-master at the Kirov Theatre. In the same year, he collaborated with Igor Tchernichov in the creation of a version of *Romeo and Juliet*, but this proved too erotic for Soviet taste and was banned for all but two performances. No doubt Baryshnikov remembered this frustration and disappointment in London the following year, where he could see that experimentation in the arts was invited, not condemned.

Until the beginning of the 1960s the Kirov was regarded as the finest ballet company in Russia. Marius Petipa and Mikhail Fokine had worked in this historical theatre, and all the Diaghilev stars had been trained at the school. The teaching remained incomparable even during the Stalin era, but ballet, like all the arts, was strait-jacketed into proscribed realism, forced to depict Soviet life optimistically and in the simplest moral terms. Eventually creative choreography was so oppressed that drama ballets deteriorated into pantomime, with dancing secondary to the often ludicrous stories. Konstantin Sergeyev, one of the greatest *danseurs nobles* of the company, became artistic director in the early 1950s, followed the party line, and resigned after being attacked in the press by the prima ballerina Galina Ulanova (often partnered by him) and other dancers who accused him of restricting their opportunities. He was persuaded to return in 1960, and by the time Baryshnikov joined the company his power was absolute. Virtually no interesting new works were brought into the repertory, and it is due to his regime that, beginning with Nureyev's defection in 1961, a number of leading dancers left the company, Makarova and Baryshnikov among them.

In 1970, returning to Leningrad after dancing at London's Festival Hall, it seemed to Baryshnikov that creative prospects were improving. He danced the role of *Hamlet* in a new work by Sergeyev (who did his best to keep Jacobson's ballets out of the repertoire) and Adam in *The Creation of the World*, choreographed by Natalia Kasatkina and Vladimir Vassiliev, which was premièred in March 1971. This was a witty and entertaining work and won Baryshnikov much praise; as a result he was offered the parts of Albrecht in *Giselle* and Prince Siegfried in *Swan Lake*. In 1972 he was promoted to principal dancer.

Also in 1972 a major event occurred in the artistic life of Leningrad—George Balanchine brought his New York City Ballet to audiences starved of modern choreography. The excitement generated was tremendous, and Baryshnikov saw all of the Balanchine and Jerome Robbins works. He was also struck by one of the dancers. 'If only I had such a partner,' he said to his photographer friend, Nina Alovert, who was to follow his example and defect to America. She recorded the remark in the book she compiled, *Baryshnikov in Russia*, when they were both established in the West. The dancer he had referred to was to become his mistress—Gelsey Kirkland.

It is interesting to read Kirkland's own first impressions of Baryshnikov. Her book, *Dancing on my Grave*, is concerned with her emotional and physical decline into drug addiction and anorexia, and she lays part of the blame squarely on Baryshnikov—indeed, the overall impression is that she blamed everyone but herself. Nevertheless, a first-hand account of a ballet class at the Kirov, however slight, gives us a privileged insight and at that point in their relationship she had no axes to grind.

Waiting apprehensively in the foyer she saw a young man in a heavy wool overcoat, his dark blond hair cut collar length, burst through the street door and dash past her. Later she recognized him at the *barre* and another spectator identified him. Finding the posture and dress of the men very different from that of the New York City Ballet dancers, she was disappointed and unimpressed. Balanchine had told her the Kirov Ballet was 'old fashioned' and she was inclined to agree. Then the older men in the class cleared the floor, and to Kirkland's amazement, Baryshnikov began to rehearse a variation from *Don Quixote*.

'His talent was beyond superlatives,' she wrote. 'He vaulted the air with no apparent preparation. His steps seemed to blur together without losing any definition.' The man beside her leant across and said with pride: 'And, you know, he's just back from vacation, still trying to get over a foot injury.'

Baryshnikov's 'lack of preparation' was later to become a point of contention with her. 'His opinion was that any dancer who needed more than half an hour to warm up was not a professional. He did not understand that we were not built the same way, that we had different physical needs.'

In *Baryshnikov at Work* he indicates that while he was in Leningrad for some time he did not live alone. Discreet in his own memoirs, he has forever been a source of gossip, and Gelsey Kirkland reiterates a commonly accepted rumour that his first serious love was Natalia Makarova, which added a piquancy for Western ballet-goers in the know when 'Misha and Natasha' (as their fans like to call them) danced together in London and New York.

The last home Baryshnikov was to have in Leningrad was on the sixth floor of a house that had belonged to a pre-revolutionary aristocrat. If the comforts were minimal by Western standards, the proportions were aesthetically pleasing with large windows and lofty ceilings, and the building faced a canal, not far from the Winter Palace.

On the surface it would seem that life was agreeable. His first Albrecht had been rapturously received. Not only did he look touchingly young in a role so often danced by older men, but his own excitement and nervousness on the occasion were transmitted to the character of the youthful nobleman deceiving the innocent peasant girl, Giselle. 'Anyone who was at Baryshnikov's first Giselle would agree, I think, that never again would we see such a spontaneously ardent Albrecht, even from Baryshnikov himself,' said Nina Alovert.

The following winter he was invited to perform the second act on television, and he took the unprecedented step of asking the Bolshoi ballerina, Natalia Bessmertsova, to dance with him, an act of audacity in a country where artists do not have the right to choose their partners except in special circumstances. In spite of this and other attempts to challenge the establishment, Baryshnikov was awarded the status of Honoured Artist, which paved the way for him to have a 'creative evening' of works of his own choosing. He decided on two ballets by Mai-Esther Murdmaa, artistic director of the Estonia Theatre: *Daphnis and Chloe* with music by Ravel and Prokoviev's *The Prodigal Son*.

Baryshnikov was excited and absorbed by the preparation of the programme, frustrated by difficulties that arose, and disappointed by the audience reaction. Traditionalists complained that there was no classical *pas de deux*, and did not respond to the opening of *Daphnis and Chloe* in which Baryshnikov was seated motionless in a spotlight in silence while latecomers were still finding their seats.

It is possible that this evening was the catalyst. On 30 April 1974 Baryshnikov partnered Bessmertsova at the Kirov in *Giselle*, a gala event with every balletomane and friend and critic from both Moscow and Leningrad desperate to be in the theatre. In retrospect it turned out to be a farewell celebration of Baryshnikov's final performance in Russia. At the end of May he departed with a company of Kirov and Bolshoi artists for Canada; a month later he had made the supreme step of leaving his homeland for ever.

The Russians did not want to lose him and made an approach to him to return through Irina Kolpakova, a Kirov ballerina who had apparently accepted some form of official responsibility after his defection. The KGB kept his apartment in Leningrad for him for two years afterwards.

At first Baryshnikov decided to stay in Canada and was invited by the National Ballet of Canada to dance the part of James in *La Sylphide* (not to be confused with *Les Sylphides*)—the Scotsman who falls in love with an immortal on his wedding day. This was for television, and as soon as shooting was completed he flew to New York to replace Ivan Nagy as Makarova's partner in *Giselle* for American Ballet Theatre. He was, in the American way, instantly a star and almost as instantly categorized as a Lothario. At his request, Gelsey Kirkland,

Above *Mikhail Baryshnikov performing a splendid jété as Romeo in Kenneth MacMillan's full-length version of* Romeo and Juliet *for the Royal Ballet.*

Right *Like his compatriot Nureyev, Baryshnikov's expressive ability extends throughout the whole range of dance, from the classics to contemporary works. Here he is seen in Twyla Tharp's droll, jokey work* Push Comes to Shove.

who had only recently left New York City Ballet, was offered a contract with ABT. She was to dance at least half his performances.

He now began life as a guest artist in the West, dancing mainly with American Ballet Theatre, but appearing with the Royal Winnipeg Ballet, Pennsylvania Ballet, and the Paris Opera Ballet; he danced in Munich and Hamburg and Spoleto; he was invited to appear in Denmark and Australia, and in October 1975 London audiences had the opportunity to see him in a classic *Giselle* and a modern classic, MacMillan's *Romeo and Juliet*.

Baryshnikov's Romeo revitalized the role. Passionate, mercurial, the interpretation was utterly different from anything seen before. He brought out nuances that gave depth, mood, understanding. His entrance down the flight of stairs to the busy market-place after his secret marriage to Juliet was so starry-eyed, so ecstatic, so full of altruism towards the whole world that even Tybalt, his enemy, was included in this aura of well-being. Just as an actor brings new meaning to Shakespeare's familiar lines, so he brought startling fresh life to MacMillan's choreography. It was a revelation.

Just as Baryshnikov thrilled and stimulated audiences, so the range of work he now covered thrilled and stimulated the artist who had been so restricted in Russia, where he had been given fewer than 20 roles. He had danced regularly in only three works, *Don Quixote*, *The Creation of the World* and *Giselle*, yet now he was being offered an embarrassment of riches. Twyla Tharp, one of the most brilliant, post-modern American choreographers, created the jokey *Push Comes to Shove* for him, based on music-hall turns and in which he makes great play with a bowler hat. She choreographed a television programme for him, *Once More Frank*, which demonstrated his scope to millions who presumed he was only a classical dancer. He had the chance to choreograph himself, and that same year, 1977, his version of *The Nutcracker* was premièred by American Ballet Theatre, with *Don Quixote* to follow in 1978. He was also given the opportunity to diversify and become a film-star.

Choreographer and film director Herb Ross and his wife, the ex-ballerina Nora Kaye, were casting *The Turning Point* about a prima ballerina (Anne Bancroft) and the ballerina who had given it all up for marriage and motherhood (Shirley MacLaine). The MacLaine character's daughter was a budding dancer who joined the ballet company with ballerina Bancroft's encouragement. There she falls in love with a Russian dancer . . . and Baryshnikov was invited to (more or less) play himself.

The original intention was for the part of the girl, Emilia, to be given to Gelsey Kirkland. The off-screen romance would be reflected by the movie and would, of course, be excellent publicity. But by this time the real *affaire* was in dire straits. She was at an emotional nadir; according to herself, she binged and starved and swallowed laxatives, thyroid pills and emetics. The producers replaced her with Leslie Brown, a young dancer with ABT, and the film was not only a great hit, but Baryshnikov was nominated for an Oscar. His dance sequences— they included the balcony *pas de deux* from *Romeo and Juliet*—gave enormous awareness of the art of ballet to millions around the world who had never been inside a theatre.

With this additional public following, he joined New York City Ballet in 1978, the company that had so fired him in Leningrad six years previously. He was feeling now that he needed the discipline and security of a company committed to defined aesthetic principles, and he greatly admired Balanchine's work which dominated the repertoire. He had been very much the star with ABT, but now he wanted to be a company member on company salary.

Balanchine had been a member of the Diaghilev company, and the two men always spoke together in Russian. Baryshnikov who enjoyed the comforts of the West, was surprised by 'Mr B's' austere lifestyle. He had few possessions, almost no memorabilia, but in contrast he adored good food and wine and his diet was extremely rich—so rich, in fact, that it contributed to his heart problems, and the working relationship Baryshnikov had anticipated was threatened by Balanchine's illness and exhaustion. The company's spring season opened with Baryshnikov in a new version of Balanchine's *Apollo.* The audiences were horrified. They were expecting the original version and hated what they saw as a harshly cut and altered work. Although Baryshnikov continued to dance with the company, it was not quite as he had hoped. During his two years with New York City Ballet, he performed a variety of new roles in, among others, *Prodigal Son, Nutcracker, Jewels, Stars and Stripes* and *Fancy Free,* Jerome Robbins's highly popular work which had been developed into the film, *On the Town;* but one suspects it was with relief that his contract was amicably amended when he was invited to become the new director of ABT.

The press began the usual wild speculation as to how he would manage and what changes he would make, although on the whole they were more interested in his relationship with Jessica Lange and the rumour that Gelsey Kirkland was about to rejoin the company. She did in fact continue her personal and professional relationship with both Baryshnikov and cocaine and in May 1983 their partnership in *Giselle* was widely praised. At the same time, Baryshnikov's management of the company became increasingly under attack.

The honeymoon was over. 'The gap between Baryshnikov and the dancers

in his company is not closing,' wrote one reviewer. 'What has he done to justify
our faith? Does he really know what Ballet Theatre is all about?' said another.

Perhaps it is inevitable, within the close ballet world, that resentment always
festers. There was a certain amount of adverse reaction among serious
balletomanes that he had allowed himself to be part of a television special with
Lisa Minelli, *Baryshnikov on Broadway,* that by spreading himself in this way
he was somehow vulgarizing his talent. It may have been the direct result of
criticism that he invited Kenneth MacMillan to become Associate Artistic Director
of the company and the brilliant Alessandra Ferri to dance with it on a permanent
basis. MacMillan had already revived *Triad* for ABT before taking up the
appointment, a haunting ballet in which brotherly affection is destroyed by the
intrusion of a woman. Now he brought in *Romeo and Juliet,* the one-act version
of *Anastasia,* and created a new and tremendously successful *Sleeping Beauty.*

Baryshnikov remains in charge. He made a second movie, *White Nights,* about
a defecting dancer, and starred in Franco Zeffirelli's film of *Giselle.* In spite of
the journalistic hawks he manages to guard his privacy in his home in Connecticut.
There is a sense that the urgent need to dance and do everything after the
artistically deprived years in Russia has left him a somewhat lonely person. During
the first years in America he badly missed the friends he had left in Leningrad,
telephoning whenever it was possible despite the listening operators, aware that
the conversations were being recorded. He and they knew that, as an artist,
he had made the right decision, but the man has still to cope with two lives,
before and after.

M·E·R·L·E P·A·R·K

'**O**ur house was built on stilts and we used to play underneath, sometimes finding poisonous snakes there. The surrounding fields were full of wonderful trees with exotic fruits—papaya, granadilla, mangos. I used to think I wanted to be a hairdresser and I'd curl the leaves of the mango trees and fix them with wooden pins. We lived about five miles from the town and I had to hitch a lift into my dancing class three times a week.'

Those recollections of a carefree, almost tomboyish childhood came from one of the world's most glamorous ballerinas, Merle Park, whose distinguished career with the Royal Ballet has, since 1983, been superseded by the Directorship of the Royal Ballet School. It is difficult today to reconcile the elegant, cosmopolitan artist with the little girl playing in the bush in what was Rhodesia (now Zimbabwe), keeping her nervous mother company when her engine-driver father was away several nights at a time.

Park was several years younger than her two sisters, a late unwanted child who started dancing classes at the suggestion of the family doctor as remedial exercises for her 'growing pains'. She did not care much for her ballet classes but enjoyed the Greek dancing. Appropriately, perhaps, the last role she created in her long dancing career was the title role in Kenneth MacMillan's full-length ballet *Isadora*, based on the life of Isadora Duncan who incorporated Greek poses in the free-style dancing which excited and scandalised the world 80 years ago.

Just how expressive the classical style could be, however, was brought home to Park when one of her dancing-class colleagues in Rhodesia returned from two years' training in Britain. 'She used to be awful,' Park said, 'then she came home and amazed us all with her technique.' By the time she had reached her teens Park's own technique was sufficiently good for her teacher to advise that she, too, needed more regular and advanced tuition if she intended to be a professional dancer.

Park's parents were apprehensive at the suggestion. Where was the money to come from? Who would look after their youngest daughter thousands of miles from home? Park's teacher pressed the matter, however, and with her pupil's own enthusiasm and insistence ways and means were found to overcome such problems. The family sold their car and brought a smaller one; Merle's room was let to a paying guest and the fare to London was raised by the dancing school, which organized a benefit performance.

And so, at the tender age of 13, Park made the long voyage to Britain with two other girls and a chaperoning mother to study as a boarder at the Elmhurst Ballet School in Camberley, Surrey. One of Park's sharpest memories

is being taken to see the Royal Ballet perform *Swan Lake* at the Davis Theatre in Croydon. After the performance one of her teachers asked what she had enjoyed most and, without hesitation, Park replied 'the Neapolitan dance'. It was a highly indicative reply, providing a clue to the initial course taken by her own career. The Neapolitan dance in that particular production was choreographed by Frederick Ashton, a fast, show-stopping duet in the ballroom scene in the third act, exactly the sort of thing that Park later enjoyed doing: a brilliant show-piece that brought the house down. In her early years as a soloist with the Royal Ballet, Park's artistic philosophy might be summarized as 'Get on, get off and get home.' It was, perhaps, the result of having developed a tremendous technical facility, a virtuoso style that had been comparatively rare in British ballerinas and which was naturally exploited by the company.

After spending some time as a student with the Royal Ballet Upper School, Park entered the Royal Ballet at Covent Garden in 1954, some two years before Antoinette Sibley and three years before Lynn Seymour, although these three dancers were contemporaries of a particularly talented generation, each one of them making their mark through different and complementary qualities. Seymour was the dramatic dancer *par excellence*, Sibley was the lyrical classicist, and Park the brilliant technician.

For the first two years Park did the necessary stint in the *corps* before being made a soloist in 1956. She studied and performed most of the solo variations in the classical and Romantic repertoire, such as the fairies in the Prologue of *The Sleeping Beauty* and the peasant *pas de deux* in the first act of *Giselle*. She was very happy doing her bravura thing, content to be a virtuoso soloist before being made a principal in 1962—although she had danced several leading roles before achieving that status.

The first full-length role that Park undertook was Cinderella in Ashton's perenially popular version of the ballet. Another important Ashton role that she danced—before being made a principal—was Lise in *La Fille mal gardée*. Both roles demand a diamond-sharp brilliance of execution and charm and vivacity mixed with a dash of pathos in the characterization; but nothing very demanding in terms of dramatic expression. 'I suppose in those days I was considered not much more than a soubrette,' Park has said, and it seems then that she was content that it should be so.

Park's first performances as Aurora in *The Sleeping Beauty* were given with

Merle Park as Nikiya in Rudolf Nureyev's production of Act III of La Bayadère *for the Royal Ballet. In this photograph she is also partnered by Nureyev as the hero Solov.*

the Royal Ballet Touring Company (now Sadler's Wells Royal Ballet) as a guest artist in 1961. Of all the big classical roles it is probably the one most suited to her talents, demanding continuous solo variations, a hugely daunting supported *adage* (the Rose Adagio) and a final grand *pas de deux*, variations, and coda that are the very pinnacle of classical virtuosity. In the 1968 production of the ballet at Covent Garden by Peter Wright, Park danced Aurora six times in the four years 1968–72, sharing the role with Margot Fonteyn, Antoinette Sibley, Vyvyan Lorrayne, Jennifer Penney, and Ann Jenner. In subsequent productions her share of the role was expanded. She was also called upon many times to dance the other great virtuoso *pas de deux* in that ballet, Princess Florine, in what is generally known as the Bluebird *pas de deux*.

Between the mid-1960s and mid-1970s Park gave more performances of the title role of *Giselle* than any of the Royal Ballet's several ballerinas—no doubt because of the exhausting technical demands of the second act. But the first act, of course, necessitates a considerable histrionic ability and it is this Romantic classic that first made Park give careful consideration to her acting.

Of the one-act works demanding great bravura ability Park was particularly brilliant in *The Firebird* and that great jewel of classicism, *La Bayadère*—especially with Rudolf Nureyev as her partner. Park was chosen to dance the role of Clara in Nureyev's beautiful production of *The Nutcracker*, designed by Nicholas Georgiadis, at its first performance in 1968. In subsequent performances she danced the part more times than the other five ballerinas put together. Her partnership with Nureyev was a celebrated one and they frequently performed overseas together as guest artists with a number of companies.

The first role to be created for Park was that of the Celestial in Antony Tudor's enigmatic *Shadowplay*, a ballet partly based on Rudyard Kipling's *Jungle Book*, which had been the inspiration for Charles Koechlin's score. It is an allegory about a child of nature, The Boy With Matted Hair, who is confronted with various figures that affect his developing maturity. The Celestial is a powerful goddess, tempting him with visions of authority and sensuality, and with such an acute, fastidious, and demanding choreographer as Tudor it was no casual decision to cast Park in the role.

But it was with the later ballets of Kenneth MacMillan that Park reached her full potential as a dancer, combining her virtuosity with a theatrical expressiveness that had been overlooked in the general acceptance of her outstanding technical facility. Early in her career, in 1965, she had been the fourth cast in MacMillan's first full-length ballet, *Romeo and Juliet*, with Donald MacLeary as her partner. She had acquitted herself admirably in the role—particularly, of course, in the execution of the choreography—without reaching the emotional heights, or depths, of Seymour or Fonteyn, although with each new performance of the part there was always some small detail, some fresh approach to a sequence, that revealed a lively intelligence at work. As with all MacMillan's major roles, there is a wide margin for individual interpretation, and Park's conception was gradually developed over a number of seasons to the point where Juliet's character, changing from rebellious girl to impassioned woman, was presented with great clarity.

Nearly a decade later, in 1974, MacMillan created *Manon*, based on the novel by Abbé Prevost, and the title role of the innocent girl turned courtesan, torn between true love and a life of luxury, fitted Park's on-stage personality like a glove. With her glittering technique Park had always been able to project the epitome of sophistication and glamour, of fascinating, desirable womanhood—witness Tudor's casting of the Celestial—and Manon, emblazoned with jewels and literally manhandled by the young bucks of decadent Parisian society in the eighteenth century, gave Park the opportunity to project the allure that drove her impoverished lover, Des Grieux, to crime and degradation. This type of *femme fatale*, recurring throughout history and literature from Helen of Troy to Cleopatra, from Salome to Isolde, was the sort of role which, in her mature years, allowed Park to develop an unsuspected histrionic ability.

The facility to portray women with a fatal fascination is most probably why Park was cast in the title role of Jack Carter's ballet *Lulu*, based on Frank Wedekind's series of sensational plays which outraged German audiences in the late nineteenth century and which also inspired Alban Berg's great unfinished opera of the same title. Lulu was the symbol of used and abused womanhood, the eternally fascinating and mysterious heroine who, in Wedekind's story, ends up at the hands of Jack the Ripper. It is a theatrically difficult form, a mixture of Expressionism and allegory, melodrama and cabaret, but one which is, perhaps, uniquely suited to balletic conventions. The weak point of Carter's ballet was in his choice of music: instead of Berg's atonal score—or some musical assemblage taken from the opera—Carter chose music by the French composer Darius Milhaud which was rather too cheerful and jazzily sophisticated. Kurt Weill might have been a more suitable composer. At any rate Park scored a hit with her portrayal of the exotic and erotic heroine and added to her growing *galère* of dangerously attractive women.

Curiously, considering that the dual role of Odette-Odile poses tremendous technical hurdles, Park came late to that most popular of all the great classics, *Swan Lake*, essaying the Swan Queen and her evil mirror-image for the first time in February 1973, partnered by Desmond Kelly as Prince Siegfried. It was, as one might have expected, a technically flawless performance, the lyrical second act given a lustrous sheen in contrast to the brilliant glitter of the third act. In fact both this first performance and 23 further ones during the next four years were somewhat underestimated by the critics. The appearent ease and authority which which Park was able to approach the role tended to make people take it all very much for granted. As one ballet enthusiast remarked, 'You always feel safe with Park, she never lets you down, never makes you feel nervous.'

This tremendous reliability, of never being erratic in the quality of performances, does not, of course, come easily. It is not just the endless hard work, the daily classes, the careful preparation of major roles, however familiar— most principals follow that dedicated routine; but an attitude of mind that, in the final analysis, comes down to absolute professionalism. Even in class Park maintains an immaculate image: not for her the raggedy old practice clothes affected by a number of famous dancers, but a fresh leotard, smart sweaters, and leg-warmers that, if not exactly colour-co-ordinated, are at least not shapeless and full of holes. Watching Park rehearse is almost like watching a performance. Whereas most dancers are content to 'mark' a rehearsal—that is, to walk through the difficult bits—Park will often dance all-out, ready to go over a sequence again and again to get it right.

This dedicated professionalism resulting in the maintenance of her superb technique season after season, year after year, is probably one reason why she has so often been teamed not only with the Royal Ballet's own principals with a superlative classical style but also with such guest stars as Rudolf Nureyev and Mikhail Baryshnikov. Park was teamed with Baryshnikov for his first performance with the Royal Ballet, two of *Romeo and Juliet* and three of *Swan Lake*. It is enough to say that in this memorable season—autumn 1975—Park's dancing was not eclipsed by the world's greatest male virtuoso, then at the height of his powers. (A year before Park's position as a leading ballerina with the company had received official recognition: the award of the CBE.)

In that same year, 1974, Park had created another role in one of MacMillan's most enduring successes, the infectiously frolicsome *Elite Syncopations*, set to ragtime music by Scott Joplin and his contemporaries. Depicting the raffish and raunchy atmosphere in a Mississippi dance-hall at the turn of the century, the ballet ranges through virtuoso solos to slapstick duets; Park's roles, both in a stylish solo with top hat and cane and in an elegant duet, once again made use of her tremendous suavity, her effortlessly projected glamour.

This stylishness in everything she does is carried over into her private life.

Right Merle Park in one of the solos from Kenneth MacMillan's Isadora, *based on the life of Isadora Duncan.*

Left Merle Park as the Countess Larisch with David Wall as Crown Prince Rudolf in Kenneth MacMillan's Mayerling.

Park has been married twice, first to James Monahan, the distinguished journalist and critic who was later to become Director of the Royal Ballet School and by whom she had a son, Anthony; later she married lawyer Sidney Bloch, with whom she now lives in a charming neo-Georgian house overlooking the Thames at Chiswick. Both of them are bon viveurs, enjoying good food (Sidney is something of a gourmet chef himself) and entertaining friends, mostly from the ballet world. In latter years Sidney has given up his legal practice but handles many of Park's contracts as well as helping to run the business side of the small ballet school that Park began around the middle of her career.

The school premises were originally bought for her own use, to practise in when, for example, she was scheduled to appear with a visiting guest star like Baryshnikov who might fly in on a Sunday when the Royal Ballet studios were closed. The idea of using the studio as a ballet school came about when a close friend and colleague, Shirley Graham, gave up dancing with the Royal Ballet and, having taken a special training course, was ready to begin teaching. Graham has now taken over the running of the school—which also teaches the Greek style of dancing alongside the classical technique, just like Park's first school back in Rhodesia.

It was in two later full-length ballets by MacMillan that Park brought her acting ability to full fruition, crowning a successful career with two memorable portraits of real-life characters.

The first was Countess Larisch in *Mayerling*, the ballet which told the true, unromanticized story behind the double suicide of Crown Prince Rudolf of Austria-Hungary and his 17-year-old mistress Mary Vetsera at the royal hunting lodge at Mayerling, just outside Vienna. Countess Larisch had been the Crown Prince's mistress at Court and, after his marriage to the dowdy Princess Stephanie of Belgium, was anxious to continue the liaison. Thwarted in this, she becomes the catalyst who subsequently brings Rudolf into his fatal alliance with Mary. It is a many-faceted role, a woman who had a genuine love for the Prince but who also thrived on the many Court intrigues. Park gave the role great depth, bringing out the several aspects of the character, physically alluring, witty—one could almost imagine her cynical asides about other members of the Court— and illuminating every scene in which she appeared, especially the one in which she tells Mary's fortune with the cards, with tremendous clarity. And, of course, her dancing was thrillingly expressive in the several *pas de deux* and solos that MacMillan wrote for her. In short, it was a performance that almost stole the ballet, crammed as it was with wonderful roles for all the principals. *Mayerling* was given its world première in February 1978, and Park continued dancing the role of Larisch (she also danced Mary on a number of occasions) until January 1987, when she performed it while the Royal Ballet was appearing in Amsterdam.

The last great part created for her was the title role of *Isadora*, MacMillan's highly innovative ballet telling the life story of the famous American dancer Isadora Duncan, whose free style of movement, vaguely based on Greek dancing, taken together with her lurid life-style, scandalized society in Europe and America for some 30 years. MacMillan had originally conceived the idea for the ballet when he was Director of the Berlin Opera Ballet (Duncan had scored some of her greatest successes in that city) when Lynn Seymour was his prima ballerina. It was a part perfectly suited to Seymour's physique and temperament but when, at last, MacMillan felt he was ready to create the work using all the available resources of the Royal Ballet and the stage at Covent Garden, Seymour had decided to accept the Directorship of the Munich Ballet and so was not available for the close collaboration that MacMillan needed in creating such a long and complicated role. His choice fell on Park, whose svelte figure was hardly similar to Duncan's more rondurous shape but who had proved that her technical ability combined with a new-found authority as an actress gave her the range and presence necessary for such a demanding role. It was, in fact, a tremendous undertaking for a dancer already into her forties—an enormous test of stamina, apart from the necessary aesthetic qualities.

MacMillan's conception of the ballet proved so comprehensive that he decided to divide the role of Isadora into two parts, an acting-speaking part, played by Mary Miller, and the dancing part. In preparing *Mayerling* he had asked Gillian Freeman to create the scenario from the huge bibliography available—a welter of personal memoirs, autobiographies, historical reconstructions, police files, and medical reports. A similarly large amount of literature existed covering Duncan's lurid life, and once again he approached Freeman to devise the scenario. For the first time for many years he also commissioned an original score for the ballet, choosing Richard Rodney Bennett as the composer.

The dancing role of Isadora finally emerged as one of the longest and toughest ever created for a ballerina—hardly ever off stage and then only for a succession of quick changes. The scenario included many of the melodramatic events in Duncan's astonishingly adventurous life—her endless travels around the world, her constant *affaires*, especially with Gordon Craig, the famous theatre designer, and Paris Singer, multi-millionaire heir to the sewing-machine empire; the tragic drowning of her children, her disastrous marriage to the Russian poet Esenin, and her many dance recitals—one of them before Lenin and his Russian revolutionaries, another causing a riot in Chicago. Finally there was her bizarre death in Nice when the fringed scarf she was wearing caught in the wheels of a Bugatti and strangled her.

This extraordinary picaresque scenario demanded many styles of dance, from long, classically-based *pas de deux* with the many men in her life and pastiche solos created in Duncan's own free-flowing form to the tango and popular dances of the 1920s. The ballet was premièred as part of the fiftieth anniversary celebrations by the Royal Ballet in 1981 and although it received mixed, and sometimes diametrically opposed, reviews from the critics most of them acknowledged that it was a personal triumph for Park, a fitting pinnacle to her career. It was a long, long way from being 'just a soubrette'.

In 1983 Park was appointed as Director of the Royal Ballet School, a position of enormous responsibility and, of course, immensely time-consuming. Nevertheless, she continued dancing important roles—Nikiya in *La Bayadère*, Countess Larisch in *Mayerling*—for several seasons and, as this is written, she has resumed taking daily class so there might still be the prospect of seeing this great dancer in suitable character parts, if not as a prima ballerina.

In 1986 Merle Park was created a Dame of the British Empire in the Birthday Honours List.

F·U·R·T·H·E·R R·E·A·D·I·N·G

Bland, Alexander, *The Nureyev Image* (Studio Vista, 1976)

Bland, Alexander, *The Royal Ballet, The First Fifty Years* (Threshold Books, 1981)

Buckle, Richard, *Nijinsky* (Weidenfeld & Nicholson, 1971)

Demidov, Alexander, *The Russian Ballet, Past and Present* (A. & C. Black, 1978)

France, C. Engell (ed.), *Baryshnikov at Work* (New York, 1981)

Galina Ulanova, A Biography (Moscow, 1956)

Gruen, John, *Erik Bruhn, Danseur Noble* (Viking Press, 1979)

Kahn, A., *Days with Ulanova* (New York and London, 1962)

Kaye, Nora, various articles in *American Ballet Theatre* (A. & C. Black, 1978)

Kerensky, Oleg, *Anna Pavlova* (London, 1973)

Kirstein, Lincoln, *Thirty Years, The New York City Ballet* (A. & C. Black, 1979)

Krasovskaya, V., *Anna Pavlova* (Leningrad, 1964)

Lifar, Serge, *Ma Vie*, tr. by James Holman Mason (Hutchinson, 1975)

Makarova, Natalia, *A Dance Biography* (Knopf, 1979)

Markova, Alicia, *Markova Remembers* (Hamish Hamilton, 1987)

Martins, Peter, *Far from Denmark, An Autobiography* (Boston, 1982)

Monahan, James, *Fonteyn* (London, 1957)

Money, Keith, *The Art of Margot Fonteyn* (London, 1965)

Newman, Barbara, *Striking a Balance* (Elm Tree Books, 1982). Interviews with (among others) Lynn Seymour, David Wall and Peter Martins

Nijinsky, Romola, *Nijinsky* (Gollancz, 1933; Simon & Schuster, 1934)

The Diary of Vaslav Nijinsky (Penguin)

Nureyev, Rudolf, *Nureyev, An Autobiography* (Hodder & Stoughton, 1962)

Selby-Lowndes, J., *The Blue Train: The Story of Anton Dolin* (London, 1953)

Seymour, Lynn, *Lynn, An Autobiography* (Granada, 1984)

Smakov, G., *Baryshnikov: From Russia to the West* (New York, 1981)

Thorpe, Edward, *Kenneth MacMillan, The Man and the Ballets* (Hamish Hamilton, 1985)

Vaughan, David, *Frederick Ashton and his Ballets* (A. & C. Black, 1977)

I·N·D·E·X